Your First Amateur Radio HF Station

**From Antennas to Amplifiers
—Everything You Need to Know!**

Published by

ARRL
100
YEARS

by Steve Ford, WB8IMY

Production
Jodi Morin, KA1JPA
David Pingree, N1NAS
Shelly Bloom, WB1ENT

Cover Design
Sue Fagan, KB1OKW

Stefan Gustavsson, SA0BFN, operating a small station aboard the icebreaker ship Saint Eric in Stockholm, Sweden. The station shown here is typical of smaller, more modest HF stations that many amateurs enjoy, especially their first stations. [Photo by Henryk Kotowski, SM0JHF]

Table of Contents

Foreword

HF operating has been at the heart of Amateur Radio from the very beginning and remains so to this day. That's not to say that HF bands are necessarily superior to frequencies above 50 MHz. In fact, many would argue that ham radio on VHF and above is more technically challenging.

However, the allure of HF is found in the fact that you can communicate over great distances with relative ease, almost any time of the day or night. And unlike VHF+, the effectiveness of HF communication isn't as greatly affected by the height of nearby objects such as hills, mountains, or buildings. At HF almost any antenna in any environment will "work." When conditions are favorable, you can talk to the other side of the world on HF frequencies with little more than a wire tossed into a tree.

If you're reading this book it is safe to assume that you're making your first forays into HF communications. Perhaps you're a newly licensed amateur, or maybe you've spent a long ham career at VHF and you've decided to try your hand at lower frequencies. Either way, this book is your guide to setting up an HF station in a way that will allow you to get the most enjoyment possible.

This book assumes that you want to start relatively small, creating a foundation that you can build upon over the years. "Small" can mean many things, but it doesn't necessarily mean ineffective. There are hams operating in apartments who've worked more than 100 DX Century Club entities and have the certificates hanging on their walls to prove it. They achieved their goals through combinations of skill and technical savvy. They compensated for the limitations of their stations by optimizing their antenna choices and by operating with modes such as CW and PSK31 to get the greatest "bangs for their bucks."

Also, while Amateur Radio has the potential to be an expensive passion, it doesn't have to be that way. You can own an HF station that will give you endless operating enjoyment for less money than you might imagine. It is simply a matter of making the right choices.

David Sumner, K1ZZ
ARRL Chief Executive Officer
February 2014

Chapter 1

Antenna Choices

When planning and budgeting for your first HF station, the antenna system must be at the top of your list. That's why this chapter occupies the largest amount of space in the book.

As you consider your antenna options, keep the following thought foremost in mind:

The quality of my antenna system will have the greatest impact on the effectiveness of my station.

Almost nothing else you will purchase will be more important than your antenna and the cable that connects it to your radio. Together we call them the "antenna system."

Don't become hypnotized by the glitz and gee-whiz glitter of modern transceivers. They are beautiful to look at and fun to operate, but you'll never get a decent return on your investments if you connect them to poor antenna systems.

As an object lesson, consider home audio enthusiasts. It is truly sad to see some of them wasting hundreds and even thousands of dollars on gorgeous amplifiers, which they proceed to connect to substandard speakers. They don't realize that the speakers dictate how the entire system will sound! Experienced audio hobbyists and professionals know that they are far better off sinking their funds into top-quality speaker systems before they even *think* of purchasing high-end amplifiers. The same is true when it comes to your station transceiver and its antenna. If you have limited funds (don't we all?), put as much money as possible into your antenna system. You'll be glad you did.

Of course, the type of antenna system you'll choose will depend not only on money, but also on the nature of your station environment — including whether you're limited to installing antennas indoors or out.

Outdoor Antennas

You don't need to live on acres of property to erect an effective HF antenna outdoors. Instead, the key consideration is *support*. All antennas have to be supported in some fashion, but support can consist of trees, poles, metal towers, fences, and even your home or apartment building. After you've read through this section, take a walk outside your home and look around. Use your imagination and visualize various types of antennas and how they might fit into the space you have available. You might also bring a note pad and a tape measure to help map your options. I can almost guarantee that no matter how small your property happens to be, you *can* set up a useful antenna — perhaps even more than one antenna.

Verticals

If you are severely cramped for space, it is hard to beat a vertical antenna. Unlike a typical wire antenna that may require 10s of feet of horizontal space, a vertical needs only a couple of square feet at its base — unless you count the *radial wires*, although they are usually buried in the soil and out of sight. A vertical antenna relies on these radial wires to create a path for return currents.

In the crudest sense of the word, a vertical antenna is simply a vertically oriented metal tube or wire. It doesn't require support because it supports itself. The vertical can be a ¼ wavelength long, or it might be ⅝ wavelength, or any other length that can be matched to the feed line. One conductor of the feed line is attached to the vertical radiating element of the antenna and the remaining conductor is attached to the ground plane, which usually consists of wires known as *radials*.

When compared to horizontal antennas, verticals suffer more acutely from two types of losses: *ground return losses* for currents in the near field, and *far-field ground losses*. Ground losses in the near field can be minimized by using many ground radials. Far-field losses are highly dependent on the conductivity and dielectric constant of the earth around the antenna, extending out as far as 100 wavelengths from the base of the antenna. There is very little that someone can do to change the character of the ground that far away — other than moving to a small island surrounded by saltwater!

The Butternut HF9V multiband vertical antenna.

But very few of us have salt marshes or beaches on our properties, so if we're considering ground mounted verticals we must also consider the prospect of laying down a number of radial wires as well. This conjures visions of spending hours on your knees, tediously burying dozens of long wires under your lawn. Suddenly the space requirements of a dipole don't seem so bad!

Take heart. Recent research has shown that for Amateur Radio applications it is not necessary to establish giant networks of radials in your soil. In the March 2010 issue of *QST* magazine there is an article by Rudy Severns, N6LF, titled "An Experimental Look at Ground Systems for HF Verticals." In the article Rudy demonstrates that you can enjoy perfectly acceptable vertical antenna performance with a modest number of radials (20 seems to be a good number).

The old saw about radials having to be ¼ wavelength at the lowest operating frequency has also proven to be false. The lengths of the radial wires appear to be less important than the *total number* of wires. Bottom line: put down as many radials as your time and patience allow and make them as long as your space allows. Don't go overboard, since you'll reach the point of diminishing returns fairly quickly. If you can place only four 30-foot radial wires, do it. If you can place 20 wires, but they are all only 10 feet in length, that's fine, too. Yes, more radials on the ground will improve your antenna performance, but for casual operating (as opposed to competitive DXing or contesting) the benefits of a large radial network are questionable.

Placing radial wires in a perfect circle on the ground around the base of the antenna is ideal, but if you can't achieve that, don't worry. Lay the wires any way you can — straight, zigzag or whatever. Your antenna's radiation pattern won't be perfectly omnidirectional, but in all likelihood you'll never notice.

Are you reluctant to dig channels in your lawn for the radial wires? I can't blame you. The good news is that you can let Mother Nature do the work for you. The trick is to chop up some very stiff wire into V or U shaped pieces better known as "garden staples." At the time of this writing, you could also purchase these staples from vendors such as Ross Radio at **http://radialstaple.wordpress.com**. Stretch out your radial wires on the ground and place the staples every foot or so to hold the wires in place. Over the coming months, the grass will gradually grow over the radials and bury them for you!

Radial wires can be bare or insulated. Insulated wires will have greater longevity by virtue of reduced corrosion and dissolution from soil chemicals. Hardware cloth and chicken wire are also quite effective, although the galvanizing must be of high quality to prevent rapid rusting. Steer clear of aluminum wire as this will corrode to powder in most soils.

Also resist the urge to rely on ground rods. This is the ground system of absolute last resort, and it is a poor one at that. A single ground rod, or a group of them bonded together, is seldom as effective as a collection of random-length radial wires.

The Monoband Vertical

If you are interested only in operating on a single band, a ¼ wavelength monoband vertical may fit the bill. You can use the following equation . . .

$$\text{Length} = 234 \,/\, \text{Frequency (MHz)}$$

. . . to calculate the length of the antenna, although keep in mind that the result is an approximation. As they say in automobile commercials, your mileage may vary.

The antenna can be made from metal mast sections (I once made a 20-meter vertical from 16 feet of electrical conduit). Alternatively, you could place a 12-gauge wire inside a tube made from sections of PVC tubing and achieve the same result, with the advantage that wire is much easier to trim if you need to adjust for the lowest SWR.

An end-fed metal radiator must be insulated from ground unless special matching techniques are used. If you choose to build your antenna from mast sections and you decide to the clamp the antenna to a metal pipe that you've hammered into the soil, make sure the outside of the pipe is covered with an insulating material (wrapping it with electrical tape will do for a while, but a sleeve of PVC pipe is a better long-term insulator).

As you plan your vertical, consider the fact that the antenna may be vulnerable in high winds. I've seen 43-foot verticals survive 60 MPH sustained winds with little difficulty. For taller antennas you may need to consider guy wires (or just Dacron line) spaced at equidistant points around the base of the antenna, attaching at the middle with an insulated ring or clamp.

Multiband Verticals

With a little assistance from a remote automatic antenna tuner, a multiband vertical is remarkably easy to build.

The design shown in **Figure 1.1** is based on a 33-foot radiator. This is about ¼ wavelength on 40 meters. The remote antenna tuner is installed at the base of the antenna. If the tuner isn't fully weatherproof, you'll need to provide some sort of watertight enclosure. Of course, this antenna will

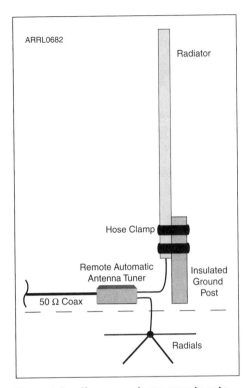

Figure 1.1 — If you can place a remote automatic antenna tuner at the base of a vertical antenna, you'll enjoy multiband operation. In this example, a 33-foot vertical can be used on 40 through 10 meters.

also require a network of radial wires on the ground.

The antenna tuner will have an easy time tuning this antenna on 40 meters since the impedance will already be close to 50 Ω at the base. The tuner will also likely find an acceptable match on 30, 20, 17, 15, 12, and 10 meters. Depending on the design of the tuner you've chosen, it may even match the antenna on 80 meters, although the antenna is only ⅛ wavelength at this frequency.

If a 33-foot radiator is too tall, consider a 16 foot design. With the antenna tuner at the base, you'll likely be able to operate on all bands from 20 through 10 meters. It may function on 40 meters as well, but once again, it will be only ⅛ wavelength at this frequency.

As you comb through the ham literature you'll stumble across references to 43-foot vertical antennas. Forty-three feet may seem like an odd length for a vertical antenna since it isn't a ¼ wavelength on any amateur band except 60 meters. The idea behind the 43-foot vertical is to create an antenna that creates feed point impedances that fall within the ranges of most remote automatic antenna tuners on *every* HF band. This length also provides low angle radiation, good for DX, on 160 through 20 meters where it is the optimum length. While this approach can certainly work, bear in mind that a 43-foot vertical is electrically short on 80 and 160 meters. A remote tuner will probably be able to find a match, but don't expect barn-burning performance on these bands. Your signal could be as much as 10 dB down from those running "full-sized" antennas on 80 and 160 meters.

Commercial Verticals

With so many amateurs living under the burden of antenna restrictions, a number of commercial vendors have brought vertical antennas to market. You'll find 43-foot verticals including "packages" that combine both the antenna and the remote automatic antenna tuner. Remember that you can use a remote tuner with any single-radiator vertical, regardless of its length.

You'll also find verticals that dispense with the antenna tuner at the base and instead use a 4:1 UNUN — a unbalanced to unbalanced transformer —

Verticals on Roofs

If you don't have enough room for a vertical antenna on the ground, consider your roof. Elevated verticals can actually perform very well, rivaling dipole antennas in many instances, but there are several drawbacks.

The most obvious problem is visibility. A tall vertical antenna on your rooftop will be highly visible to the entire neighborhood. Don't be surprised if it draws questions from your neighbors, or even complaints. (People are particularly concerned about anything that appears to harm the "look" of a neighborhood, resulting in reduced property values.)

A rooftop vertical antenna still requires radial wires. If you erect a single-band vertical, you'll need to attach two to four wires, and each must be cut to approximately ¼ wavelength for the band in question. As with a dipole antenna, you will need to carefully trim or lengthen the wires until you achieve the lowest SWR at your desired frequency. If you install a multiband vertical, you'll need at least one ¼ wavelength radial wire for each band. As you might imagine, tuning an antenna in this fashion while negotiating a steep roof would be a challenge (to put it mildly). The exception would be an antenna such as the Cushcraft R9 that provides shortened radial rods at its base.

Safely securing an HF vertical antenna to a roof presents another challenge. Do not attempt to use your chimney as a support. Chimneys were never designed to survive the wind loading stress a large vertical antenna would inflict. Instead, use a roof tripod (available at RadioShack and elsewhere) or consider side mounting the antenna at the edge of the roof using brackets that attach to the eaves of the house.

Finally, there is the problem of increased interference and RF exposure. With the antenna so close to your house, you may find that you'll suffer much more interference to your consumer electronic devices, or much more interference from them.

to convert the impedance values at the antenna input. You still need an antenna tuner, but the tuner can reside indoors next to your radio (or if your radio has a built-in tuner, that may suffice). The downside of this approach is that you must use low-loss coaxial cable such as Belden 9913 or LMR 400 between the antenna and your station. High SWR values will be present on the feed line and without low-loss cable much of your power will effectively disappear.

Other commercial vertical designs rely on traps or cleverly constructed tuning sections to allow multiband operation. These antennas work well and don't require antenna tuners, although your operation will be restricted to the available bands and to the 2:1 SWR frequency ranges within each band. These antennas are also more mechanically complicated and challenging to install. The Cushcraft R9 antenna is a good example of a vertical antenna that incorporates a series of traps for multiband operation (40 through 6 meters).

The R9 also avoids the need for ground radials by providing seven short radials at the base. Note that the base of this antenna must be installed at least 10 feet above the ground. It is debatable how well this small radial system performs compared to traditional radials. In most instances, verticals with longer in-ground radials offer superior performance. An exception is verticals that operate as an electrical half wave. These act like vertical dipoles and thus don't need a ground as part of the antenna. However, if you are considering a vertical antenna installed on your roof, the R9 and similar designs offer a strong advantage when you contemplate the prospect of spending hours on your roof carefully trimming the radials of a conventional vertical.

One of the more unusual vertical antenna designs of recent years debuted with the Fluidmotion SteppIR antenna. This vertical is comprised of a hollow fiberglass tube that contains a long beryllium tape that's perforated on both sides like old fashioned movie film. At the base of the tube is an electric stepping motor that adjusts the length of the copper tape in response to commands from a microprocessor-based controller back in the station. The result is an antenna that literally changes its length according to the band you've chosen!

The SteppIR concept has become quite popular in the amateur community. It has expanded to include SteppIR Yagi antennas that adjust their electrical lengths in similar fashion. Both the Yagis and the vertical antennas seem to hold up well in temperature and wind extremes despite their reliance on moving parts. Because of their mechanical complexity, SteppIR antennas are expensive (at the time this book went to press, the 20 — 6 meter SteppIR "SmallIR" vertical was selling for $640). They also require you to install a multiconductor control cable in addition to the feed line.

Dipoles

A dipole antenna consists of two conductors, or "poles," hence the name. Like vertical antennas, dipoles are omnidirectional radiators, which is another way of saying that they send and receive in all directions (more or less) at once. Dipoles have long been favorites because they are effective and easy to set up. You can make a dipole out of simple wire or even copper pipe — the combinations are limited only by your imagination.

The Classic Multiband Dipole

When it comes to HF antennas, many hams prefer multiband designs. After all, if you have little room for antennas to begin with, it makes sense to erect one antenna that covers as many frequencies as possible.

A example of 450-Ω "windowed" ladder line.

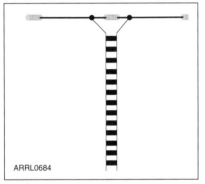

ARRL0684

Figure 1.2 — The classic multiband dipole antenna. Simply make it as long as space allows and feed it with 450 Ω ladder line. With a good antenna tuner you'll be able to operate on several HF bands.

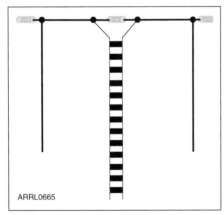

ARRL0665

Figure 1.3 — Ladder line dipoles don't have to be installed in straight lines. You can droop the ends, for example.

One of the simplest, most effective antennas in this category is a multiband random-length dipole fed with an open-wire feed line. This design has been around for close to 100 years and it remains popular today. See **Figure 1.2**.

You'll notice that Figure 1.2 doesn't specify a length for this antenna. Here is the formula to calculate it (written with tongue firmly planted in cheek):

Antenna Length = W × R / FT

W = The amount of wire you have available
R = The amount of room available
FT = Family Tolerance factor

In other words, you want as much wire as possible, as high as possible. This antenna is not particularly "stealthy;" it is easy to see with its dangling feed line. So, the Family (or Spouse, or Neighbor) Tolerance factor may play a key role.

All kidding aside, my rule of thumb for the length of this antenna is to make it at least ½ wavelength for the lowest frequency band I intend to use. For 40 meters that would be 66 feet; for 20 meters, it would be 33 feet. As mentioned previously, the half wavelength formula is:

Length = 468 / Frequency (MHz)

If you have two trees in your yard, they will make good supports for the classic multiband dipole. If you want to use this design at a low frequency such as 3.5 MHz, but you don't have 134 feet of open space between trees, don't worry. This antenna does *not* have to be deployed in a straight, horizontal line. Take a look at **Figure 1.3**. You can bend the wires in various directions to squeeze the antenna into the available space.

If you have only one tree, put it to good use. Get one end of the antenna as high as possible and slope the rest down to the ground (**Figure 1.4**). Or

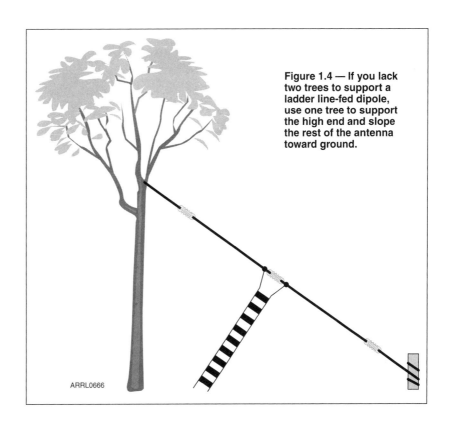

Figure 1.4 — If you lack two trees to support a ladder line-fed dipole, use one tree to support the high end and slope the rest of the antenna toward ground.

ARRL0666

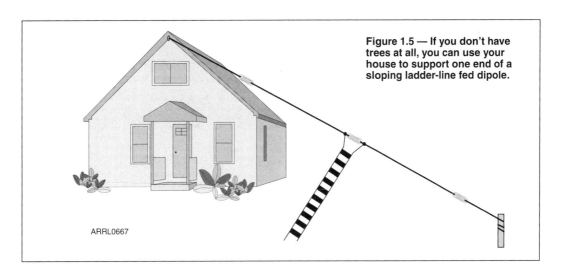

Figure 1.5 — If you don't have trees at all, you can use your house to support one end of a sloping ladder-line fed dipole.

ARRL0667

use the Inverted V approach by hauling the feed point of the antenna as high as possible and sloping both legs of the dipole to the ground.

No trees at all? No problem. Use your house to support one end and slope downward (**Figure 1.5**). Or plant a wood or metal mast in your yard (if the family will tolerate it) and use it to support one end of the dipole with the other end attached to your house (**Figure 1.6**). Just roam your property and open your mind to the possibilities that present themselves.

Most hams feed this dipole with a type of balanced line known as 450 Ω *windowed ladder line*. It is a thin, flat line with open slots in the plastic insulation spaced every inch or so, hence the "window" reference. This feed line is commonly available from Amateur Radio dealers. You'll find it for sale at hamfest fleamarkets as well. With the "station end" of the feed line connected to a wide impedance range (typically to 10:1 SWR) antenna tuner (one with a balanced input), you can find a 50 Ω impedance match for your transceiver on many bands. Yes, the SWR on the feed line between the tuner and the antenna will be very high at times, but resulting RF loss in the ladder line is usually inconsequential. You wouldn't be able to say that about ordinary coaxial cable!

With the proper antenna tuner (automatic or manual) at your radio, you'll be able to easily hop from band to band. Let's say you installed a 34-foot dipole and fed it with ladder line. With luck your tuner should be able to find an acceptable match (SWR less than 2:1) on 20 through 10 meters. Of course, depending on the variables inherent in your particular antenna installation, you may not be able to achieve a match on every band. Even

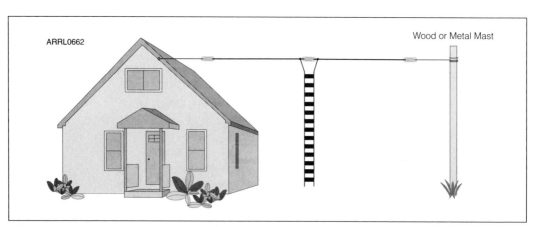

Figure 1.6 — Sometimes sloping an antenna to ground isn't a good solution, especially if you have a lot of human traffic in your yard. An alternative is to use a wood, metal or fiberglass mast to support one end and your house to support the other.

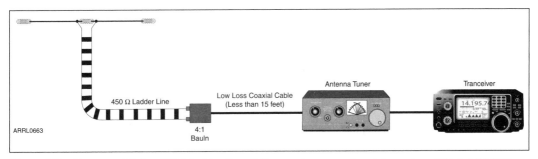

Figure 1.7 — If you can't bring 450 Ω ladder line all the way to your antenna tuner, try using a 4:1 balun, perhaps installed outside in a weatherproof enclosure. From the balun to the antenna tuner, you can use 50 Ω coaxial cable. Be sure to keep the coaxial cable short — preferably no more than 15 feet.

so, it is a good bet that you will be able to operate on several bands — all through a single antenna system.

Getting ladder line into a home and to your station can be a challenge. You must keep ladder line several inches from metal objects such as aluminum siding, electrical wiring, etc. Nearby metal upsets the balance of the RF fields that surround the feed line, resulting in an impedance mismatch.

If you don't want to bring the ladder line all the way to the radio, there are alternatives. One is shown in **Figure 1.7**. In this example we're bringing the ladder line to a 4:1 *balun* installed outside the house in a weatherproof enclosure. From the balun there is a short (10 foot) run of coaxial cable to the antenna tuner. The balun acts as a transformer to make the transition from the balanced ladder line to the unbalanced coaxial cable. That's why it is called a balun; "balun" is a contraction of "balanced-unbalanced." The balun in this example is also providing a 4:1 impedance transformation.

High SWR will exist on the length of coaxial cable and the resulting

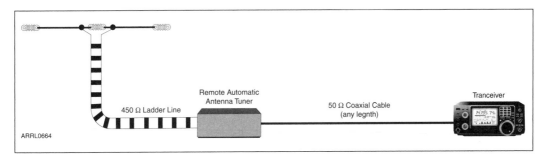

Figure 1.8 — Another approach to using an antenna tuner with a ladder line-fed dipole is purchase a remote automatic antenna tuner and place it outside near the antenna. Connect the ladder line to the tuner and then use 50 Ω coaxial cable to the radio.

loss could be substantial. That's why it must be kept as short as possible. My rule of thumb is to use low-loss coax such as Belden 9913 and not exceed 15 feet. The 4:1 impedance transformation may result, on some frequencies, in an impedance your antenna tuner can't accommodate. You could try other balun ratios such as 1:1 or even 9:1, but baluns come at a price and the cost of your experiments could begin to add up.

Another alternative appears in **Figure 1.8**. Instead of having the antenna tuner at the radio, and bringing the ladder line all the way to the station, put a remote automatic antenna tuner outside near the antenna. The ladder line would connect to the tuner and the tuner would find the low SWR match at that point. From the tuner, ordinary coaxial cable would make the rest of the journey to the radio.

Remote autotuners can be expensive, typically ranging from $200 to $500. Depending on the design and power level, you may need to run separate wiring to provide dc power and/or control signals. The lower priced tuners are rated only at about 100 W, so you wouldn't be able to use it with an RF power amplifier.

An internal view of a typical 4:1 balun.

Shopping for an Antenna Tuner

If you determine that you need an antenna tuner, you'll find there are many available. Despite the bewildering number to choose from, they can be reduced to just a few categories, according to how they function.

• **Manual Tuners:** As the name implies, you operate these antenna tuners by hand, twisting knobs and watching the SWR meter until you achieve the best match. These are among the least expensive models, but they are also the least convenient to operate. If you think you'll want to change bands and frequencies quickly, a manual tuner may not be the best choice.

• **Automatic Tuners:** These tuners have automated the tuning process. You simply apply RF and push a button — the tuner rapidly searches through combinations of inductance and capacitance until it finds the values that render the best match. Some models will respond as soon as they detect a signal from your radio — no button pushing required. Other models connect to your transceiver so that they "know" when a band change has occurred.

• **Remote Automatic Tuners:** These tuners are designed to be installed outdoors at the antenna. By achieving the best SWR at the antenna, remote tuners minimize RF loss in the cable between the antenna and the station. Remote automatic tuners will operate when they detect RF, or when they receive a command from the transceiver.

When shopping for a tuner, be sure to check its impedance range. The impedance range is critical to the tuner's ability to match a wide array of loads. Most antenna tuners that you find built into transceivers can handle only mismatches that result in 3:1 SWRs, maximum. In contrast, wide-range antenna tuners will handle SWRs of 10:1 or more.

Also pay attention to the tuner's RF power rating. For example, you may find a tuner rated for 150 W PEP — peak envelope power. This is an expression of RF power commonly used when we're talking about SSB signals. A 150 W PEP rating is fine for SSB, a signal with rapidly changing power levels, but what about a signal with a power level that is maintained continuously? An RTTY (radio

teletype) signal is said to be "100 % duty cycle," which is another way of saying that it is at maximum power continuously during the entire transmission. An antenna tuner rated for 150 W PEP is not necessarily able to safely handle 150 W at a 100% duty cycle. Check the specifications carefully. Look for language such as, "150 W SSB, 80 W CW." In this example "CW" doesn't mean a Morse code transmission; it refers to "continuous wave" in the literal sense, meaning 100% duty cycle. If you plan to operate RTTY or other 100% duty cycle mode, be sure your antenna tuner is rated for the power.

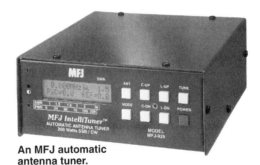

An MFJ automatic antenna tuner.

This small MFJ manual antenna tuner lacks an SWR meter. If your transceiver doesn't have an SWR meter built in, you would need to have a stand-alone meter in the line between the tuner and the radio.

A Palstar manual antenna tuner.

Coax-Fed Inverted V and Sloping Dipoles

If multiband operation isn't your top priority, there is no need to feed a dipole with open-wire line, or even use an antenna tuner. You could simply install a standard "flat top" dipole between two supports and feed it at the center with the 50-Ω coaxial cable of your choice (**Figure 1.9**). When erected

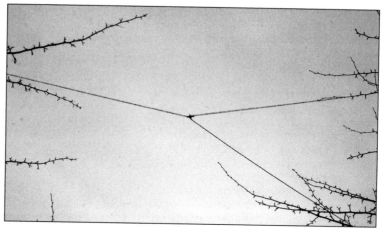

A dipole antenna fed with coaxial cable.

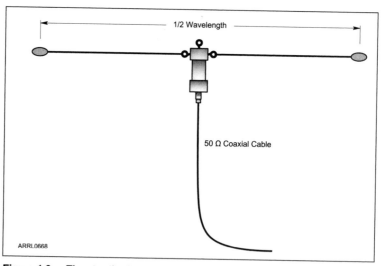

Figure 1.9 — The standard coaxial fed "resonant" dipole antenna. This antenna needs to be ½ wavelength for the band of your choice. It can be fed directly with 50 Ω coaxial cable without an antenna tuner.

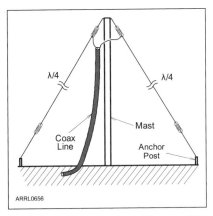

Figure 1.10 — A single-band Inverted-V antenna. Keeping the ends about 8 feet above ground will help reduce ground losses.

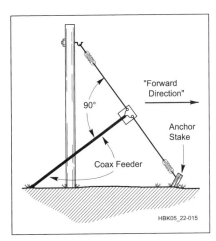

Figure 1.11 — If you have only one support, consider the sloping single-band dipole. Note the direction of radiation.

in horizontal fashion at a sufficient height, this antenna should provide a decent impedance match on one band (or in the case of a 40-meter dipole, two bands since it is often resonant on 15 meters as well, especially if you trim it at the low end of 40). You will probably have to lengthen or trim both ends of the antenna to achieve the lowest SWR; the 468/F formula will only get you within "spitting distance."

Unless you have enough room to accommodate a horizontal dipole you'll need to consider alternatives. High on the list of single-band designs are the Inverted V and sloping dipoles.

An Inverted-V dipole (**Figure 1.10**) is supported at the center with a single support, such as a tree or mast. Not only are you spared from having to find two supports with the proper separation, the fact that the legs of the Inverted-V dipole slope downward makes it easier to fit this antenna into a small lot.

The inverted-V's radiation pattern and feed point impedance depend on the *apex angle* between the legs. As the apex angle decreases, so does feed point impedance, and the radiation pattern becomes less directive. At apex angles below 90°, the antenna efficiency begins to decrease substantially.

The proximity of ground to the antenna ends will lower the resonant frequency of the antenna so that a dipole cut to the standard formula may have to be shortened in the inverted-V configuration. Losses in the ground also increase when the antenna ends are close to the ground. Keeping the ends eight feet or higher above ground reduces ground loss and also prevents humans and animals from coming in contact with the antenna.

Keeping in mind that antenna current produces the radiated signal, and current is maximum at the dipole center, you'll get the best performance by installing the center of the antenna as high as you can get it. In Figure 1.10 the Inverted V is shown being supported by a pole, but it can also be supported by a tree, or even by your house. Just avoid getting the antenna too close to metal objects.

Sloping dipoles take advantage of the fact that you may only have one tall support. This type of antenna can be created in a single-band version and fed with coaxial cable. What is interesting about the sloping dipole is that it can be used to skew your radiation pattern in a particular direction. See **Figure 1.11**. With a non-conducting support and poor ground, signals off the back are weaker than those off the front.

A conductive support such as an aluminum-sided house or a metal mast acts as a parasitic element. (So does the coax shield, unless it is routed at 90° from the antenna.) The parasitic effects vary with ground quality and support height. With such variables, performance is very difficult to predict. Losses increase as the antenna ends approach the support or the ground, so the same cautions about the height of the antenna ends applies as for the Inverted-V antenna. To prevent feed line radiation, route the coax away from the feed point at 90° from the antenna as far as possible.

The Half-Wave Vertical Dipole

Who said that a dipole had to be horizontal or sloping? Couldn't a dipole be vertical instead?

You bet it can!

If you have a tall tree in your yard, and if you can a get rope over one of the high branches, nothing would stop you from installing a dipole antenna in a vertical orientation (**Figure 1.12**). Height is the issue, however. To put up a vertical dipole for 40 meters, you'd better have a strong branch that is at least 74 feet high so that there is enough vertical space for the dipole, leaving an 8-foot gap between the end and the ground. Also, you need to bring the 50-Ω coaxial feed line away from the antenna horizontally for a substantial distance.

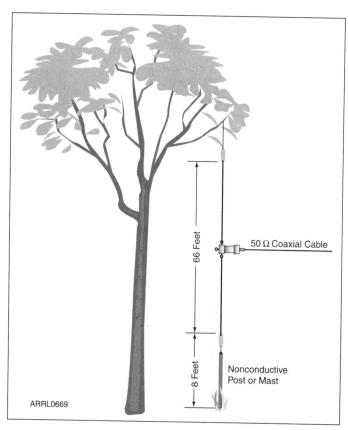

66 Feet

50 Ω Coaxial Cable

8 Feet

Nonconductive Post or Mast

ARRL0669

Figure 1.12 — If you have a tall tree handy, a dipole can just as easily be installed vertically. This illustration shows a single-band dipole fed with 50 Ω coaxial cable, but you would also suspend a ladder-line fed dipole in the same manner. Either way, try to bring the feed line away from the antenna at a 90 degree angle.

Multiband Coaxial-Fed Dipoles

For the moment let's assume that you have some horizontal space at your disposal between two supports — two trees, a single tree and a house, a tree and a mast, or whatever. Depending on how much space is available, it is possible to install a multiband dipole antenna and feed it with a single coaxial cable. It all depends on how you wish to approach the problem.

Parallel Dipoles

See **Figure 1.13**. This is certainly an odd-looking antenna, but there is a method to its madness.

Consider the center-fed dipole. It has a low feed point impedance (something close to 50 Ω) near the fundamental frequency and odd harmonics (around 120 Ω on 15). That's why a 40-meter (7 MHz) dipole can also be used at 15 meters (21 MHz). The 15-meter frequency is an odd (third) harmonic of the 7 MHz frequency. High impedances exist at other frequencies. This impedance arrangement lets us construct simple multiband systems that automatically select the appropriate antenna.

Think about a 50-Ω resistor connected in parallel with a 5-kΩ resistor. A generator connected across the two resistors will see 49.5 Ω, and 99% of the current will flow through the 50-Ω resistor (**Figure 1.14**). When resonant and non-resonant antennas are connected in parallel, the same result occurs: The non-resonant antenna has a high impedance, so little current flows in it

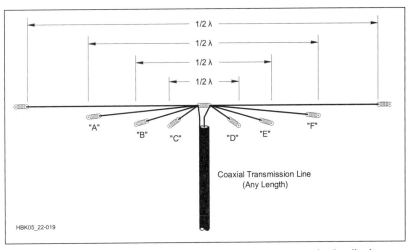

Figure 1.13 — The parallel or "fan" dipole. When it works correctly, the dipole that is resonant at the operating frequency presents the lowest impedance to the RF current.

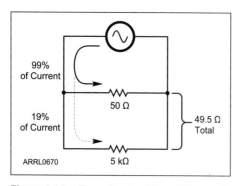

Figure 1.14 — To understand how RF current flows in a parallel dipole system, consider two resistors connected in parallel. The generator (your transceiver) is connected across both. At the resonant frequency the 50 Ω resistor (dipole) receives 99% of the current.

and it has little effect on the total feed point impedance. As a result, we can connect several dipoles together at the feed point, and power naturally flows to the resonant antenna (**Figure 1.15**).

There is no such thing as a free lunch, though. Wires in proximity to each other tend to couple due to mutual inductance. In parallel dipoles, this means that the resonant length of the shorter dipoles lengthens a few percent. The shorter antennas don't affect longer ones much, so trim the individual dipoles for resonance *in order from longest to shortest*.

Mutual inductance also reduces the bandwidth of shorter dipoles, so you may need an antenna tuner at the station to achieve an acceptable SWR across all bands covered. These effects can be reduced by

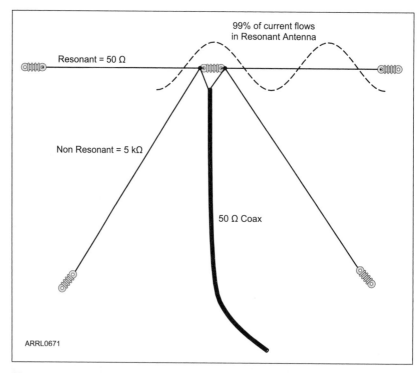

Figure 1.15 — A group of parallel dipoles behaves just like the parallel resistors in Figure 1.13. The resonant 50 Ω dipole receives most of the current.

The center feed point of a five band parallel dipole antenna. Notice the five vertically separated wires on each side of the center connector.

spreading the ends of the dipoles apart. Note that perpendicular antennas have no coupling.

Also, the power-distribution mechanism requires that only one of the parallel dipoles is near resonance on any amateur band. Separate dipoles for 80 and 30 meters should not be connected in parallel because the higher band is near an odd harmonic of the lower band (80/3 ≈ 30) and center-fed dipoles have low impedance near odd harmonics. (The 40 and 15 meter bands have a similar relationship.) This means that you either have to accept the performance of the low-band antenna operating on a harmonic or erect a separate antenna for those odd-harmonic bands. For example, four parallel-connected dipoles cut for 80, 40, 20, and 10 meters (fed by a single antenna tuner unit and coaxial cable) work reasonably on all HF bands from 80 through 10 meters.

Trap Dipoles

Trap dipoles (also called "trapped dipoles") provide multiband operation from a coax-fed single-wire dipole. **Figure 1.16** shows a two-band trap antenna. A trap consists of inductance and capacitance in parallel with a resonant frequency on the higher of the two bands of operation. The high impedance of the trap at its resonant frequency effectively disconnects the wire beyond the trap, not unlike a mechanical switch. So, on the higher of the two bands of operation at which traps are resonant, only the portion of the antenna between the traps is active.

Above resonance, the trap presents a capacitive reactance. Below

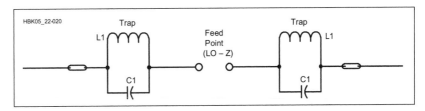

Figure 1.16 -- A two-band trap antenna. A trap consists of inductance and capacitance in parallel with a resonant frequency on the higher of the two bands of operation. The high impedance of the trap at its resonant frequency effectively disconnects the wire beyond the trap.

resonance, the trap is inductive. On the lower of the two bands of operation, then, the inductive reactance of the trap acts as a loading coil to create a shortened or loaded dipole with the wire beyond the trap.

A trap dipole is a reasonable solution when you want to operate on several bands with a single antenna in less horizontal space than you'd normally need. On the other hand, the 2:1 SWR bandwidth on each band tends to be somewhat narrow, and changing the frequency coverage within each band can be difficult. Also, if visibility is a concern, be forewarned that trap dipoles are very easy to see compared to a single, trapless wire suspended in the air.

OCF — Off Center Fed Dipole

Earlier I stated that the impedance at the center of a dipole antenna was somewhere in the neighborhood of 50 Ω. When attached to a 50 Ω coaxial cable, the resulting SWR tends to be low (below 2:1), the transceiver loads its full output into the antenna system and all is right with the world.

But there is no law that dictates that you must feed a dipole at its center. If you feed the dipole at a different point, you will encounter a different

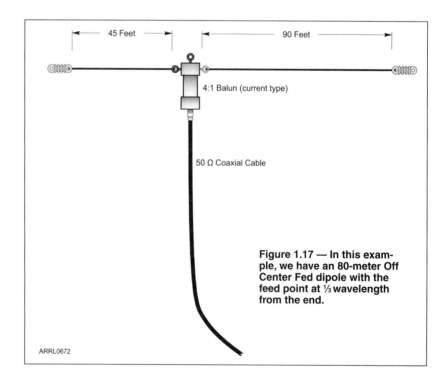

Figure 1.17 — In this example, we have an 80-meter Off Center Fed dipole with the feed point at ⅓ wavelength from the end.

impedance, but it is still possible to match that impedance to a 50 Ω coaxial line.

In **Figure 1.17** you'll see an Off Center Fed dipole design in which the feed line connects ⅓ of its length from one end. This antenna can be used on its fundamental and *even* harmonics. For this antenna, the impedance at 3.5, 7, and 14 MHz is on the order of 150 to 200 Ω. A 4:1 balun at the feed point should offer a reasonably good match to 50- or 75-Ω coax. Some commercially made OCF dipoles use 6:1 baluns. At the 6th harmonic, 21 MHz, the antenna is three wavelengths long and fed at a voltage loop (maximum), instead of a current loop. The feed-point impedance at this frequency is high, a few thousand ohms, so the antenna is unusable on that band.

Because the OCF dipole is not fed at the center of the radiator, the RF impedance paths of the two wires at the feed point are unequal. If the antenna is fed directly with coax, voltages of equal magnitude (but opposite polarity) are applied to the wires at the feed point. Because of unequal impedances, the resulting antenna currents flowing in the two wires will not be equal. The bottom line is that current will likely flow on the outside shield of the coaxial cable, which is not good.

How much current flows on the coax shield depends on the impedance of the RF current path down the outside of the feed line. At any rate, to prevent this from happening, you need to use a *current* or *choke* balun at the feed point, *not* a so-called *voltage* balun. Current/choke baluns are available from a number of amateur dealers. Some OCF dipole designs place the current choke part way down the coax to take advantage of the coax current as a vertical antenna.

So what is the advantage of an OCF dipole? It is primarily the ability to enjoy multiband operation with a single antenna without a highly visible feed line dangling from its center. With the OCF you can place the feed point at a more convenient location in terms of hiding it from view and routing the feed line into the house.

The Legendary G5RV Dipole

If you haven't heard of the G5RV dipole, you will. It has achieved legendary status in the amateur community with some hams ascribing almost magical properties to its design.

In truth, the virtue of the G5RV is that it is a multiband antenna that does not require a lot of space, is simple to construct, and is low in cost. The antenna was designed in England by the late Louis Varney, G5RV. See **Figure 1.18**. It can be used from 3.5 through 30 MHz. Although some amateurs claim that the antenna can be fed directly with 50-Ω coax and operate on several amateur bands with a low SWR, Varney himself recommended

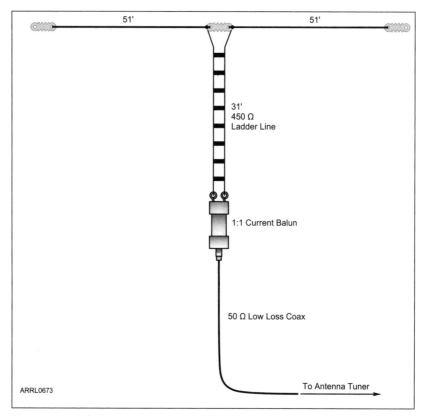

Figure 1.18 — The legendary G5RV dipole antenna.

the use of an antenna tuner on bands other than 14 MHz. In practice, you'll find that the SWR will exceed 2:1 on most bands, so you will definitely need an antenna tuner at the radio. If your transceiver has a built-in antenna tuner, that may be sufficient.

As you'll see in Figure 1.18, the antenna is fed with a specific length of 450-Ω ladder line that connects to a 1:1 *current* or *choke* balun. From there it is standard 50-Ω coaxial cable all the way back to the station. It is a good idea to use low-loss (9913 or LMR 400) coax for this portion of the feed line

The portion of the G5RV antenna shown as horizontal in Figure 1.18 may also be installed in an Inverted-V arrangement. Or instead, up to ⅙ of the total length of the antenna at each end may be dropped vertically, semi-vertically, or bent at a convenient angle to the main axis of the antenna, to cut down on the requirements for real estate.

Building Wire Dipoles

When building any kind of wire dipole antenna one of the top considerations is the wire itself. Choosing the right type of wire for the project at hand is the key to a successful antenna — the kind that works well and stays up through a winter ice storm or a gusty spring wind storm.

When deciding what gauge of wire to use, the answer depends on strength, ease of handling, cost, availability, and visibility. Generally, antennas that are expected to support their own weight, plus the weight of the feed line, should be made from #12 AWG wire. Horizontal dipoles fall into this category. Antennas supported in the center, such as Inverted-V dipoles, may be made from lighter material, such as #14 AWG wire — the minimum size called for in the National Electrical Code.

The type of wire to be used is the next important decision. One of the strongest wires suitable for antenna service is copper-clad steel, also known as *Copperweld*. The copper coating is necessary for RF service because steel is a relatively poor conductor. Practically all of the RF current is confined to the copper coating because of the skin effect.

Copper-clad steel is outstanding for permanent installations, but it can be difficult to work with because of the stiffness of the steel core. Stranded wire made of copper-clad steel wire is also available and is more flexible and easier to work with. Solid-copper wire, either hard-drawn or soft-drawn, is another popular material. Easier to handle than copper-clad steel, solid copper is available in a wide range of sizes. It is usually more expensive, however, because it is all copper. Soft-drawn tends to stretch under tension, so you may find that your dipole seems to become longer over time!

Enamel-coated *magnet-wire* is a suitable choice for experimental antennas because it is easy to manage, and the coating protects the wire from the weather. Although it stretches under tension, the wire may be pre-stretched before final installation and adjustment. A local electric motor rebuilder might be a good source for magnet wire.

Hook-up wire, speaker wire, or even ac lamp cord are suitable for temporary antennas. Frankly, almost any copper wire may be used, as long as it is strong enough for the demands of the installation.

Aluminum wire can be used for antennas, but is not as strong as copper or steel for the same diameter, and soldering it to feed lines requires special techniques.

Galvanized and steel wire, such as that used for electric fences, is inexpensive, but it is a much poorer conductor at RF than copper and should be avoided.

Kinking, which severely weakens wire, is a potential problem when handling any solid conductor. When uncoiling solid wire of any type —

copper, steel, or aluminum — take care to unroll the wire or untangle it without pulling on a kink to straighten it. A kink is actually a very sharp twist in the wire and the wire will break at such a twist when flexed, such as from vibration in the wind.

Solid wire also tends to fail at connection or attachment points at which part of the wire is rigidly clamped. The repeated flexing from wind and other vibrations eventually causes metal fatigue and the wire breaks. Stranded wire is preferred for antennas that will be subjected to a lot of vibration and flexing. If stranded wire is not suitable, use a heavier gauge of solid wire to compensate.

Insulated vs Bare Wire

Losses are the same (in the HF region at least) whether the antenna wire is insulated or bare. If insulated wire is used, a 3% to 5% shortening from the length calculated for a bare wire is required to obtain resonance at the desired frequency. This is caused by the increased distributed capacitance resulting from the dielectric constant of the plastic insulating material. The actual length for resonance must be determined experimentally by pruning and measuring because the dielectric constant of the insulating material varies from wire to wire. Wires that might come into contact with humans or animals should definitely be insulated to reduce the chance of shock or burns.

Insulators

Wire antennas must be insulated at the ends. Commercially available insulators are made from ceramic, glass, or plastic. Insulators are available from many Amateur Radio dealers. RadioShack and local hardware stores are other possible sources. I prefer glass or ceramic insulators in situations where I will be soldering wires near the insulators; plastic has a tendency to become soft and melt in the presence of a torch or heavy duty soldering iron.

Of course, you can also make your own insulators from a variety of material including (but not limited to) acrylic sheet or rod, PVC tubing, wood, fiberglass rod, or even stiff plastic from a discarded container. **Figure 1.19** shows some homemade insulators. Ceramic or glass insulators will usually outlast the wire, so they are highly recommended for a safe, reliable, permanent installation. Other materials may tear under stress or break down in the presence of sunlight. Many types of plastic do not weather well. If your antenna ends are supported with synthetic rope, separate insulators are not needed — just count on the rope as insulation, but be sure the rope is protected from the wire wearing through it.

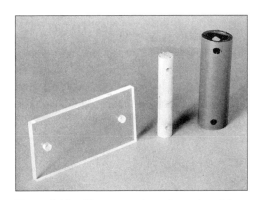

Figure 1.19 — You can make antenna insulators from just about any nonconductive materials.

Most wire antennas require an insulator at the feed point. Although there are many ways to connect the feed line, there are a few things to keep in mind. If you feed your antenna with coaxial cable, you have two choices. You can install an SO-239 connector on the center insulator and use a PL-259 on the end of your coax, or you can separate the center conductor from the braid and connect the feed line directly to the antenna wire.

Although it costs less to connect directly, the use of connectors offers several advantages. Coaxial cable braid acts as a wick to soak up water. If you do not adequately seal the antenna end of the feed line, water will find its way into the braid. Water in the feed line will lead to contamination, rendering the coax useless. It is not uncommon for water to drip from the end of the coax inside the shack after a year or so of service if the antenna connection is not properly waterproofed. Use of a PL-259/SO-239 combination (or other connector of your choice) makes the task of waterproofing connections much easier.

Another advantage to using the PL-259/SO-239 combination is that feed line replacement is much easier, should that become necessary.

Whether you use coaxial cable, ladder line, or twin lead to feed your antenna, an often overlooked consideration is the mechanical strength of the connection. Wire antennas and feed lines tend to move a lot in the breeze, and unless the feed line is attached securely, the connection will weaken with time. The resulting failure can range from a frustrating intermittent electrical connection to a complete separation of feed line and antenna. **Figure 1.20** illustrates several different ways of attaching the feed line to the antenna.

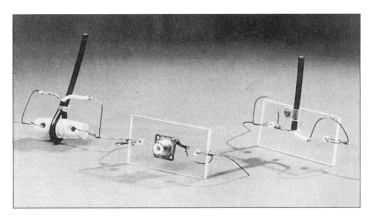

Figure 1.20 — Here are some clever designs for dipole center insulators intended for use with coaxial cable.

Commercial Dipoles

Some hams look down their noses at folks who buy their dipole antennas off the shelves rather than building them with their bare hands. Although building your own dipole saves money and is an educational process by itself, many of us simply don't have

Figure 1.21 — The Comet H-422 rotatable dipole shown in its V configuration. [Photo courtesy of the NGC Company]

the free time to buy materials and assemble dipoles.

Glance through the advertising pages of *QST* magazine and you find many dealers and manufacturers that sell dipole antennas. The designs range from simple single-band antennas fed with coaxial cable to multiband parallel dipoles. One interesting variation is provided by NCG Company — the Comet H-422 rotatable dipole (**Figure 1.21**). This is essentially a trap dipole for 40, 20, 15, and 10 meters built with aluminum tubing. It is 33 feet long horizontally, but you can raise the dipole legs to form a V, allowing the antenna to fit into a much smaller space.

Since the H-422 is supported at the center rather than at the ends like a traditional wire dipole, you can easily rotate the antenna manually or by using an electrical rotator. Dipoles have radiation patterns with gain lobes broadside to their lengths and nulls at the ends. So, rotating the H-422 allows you to position the antenna for the greatest gain in the direction you wish (or to null interference coming from other directions). At the time of this writing, the H-422 sold for $360. You'll find more information online at **www.cometantenna.com**.

The Multiband Inverted L Antenna

Hams enjoy describing antenna designs according to how they resemble letters of the English alphabet. The Inverted L antenna looks like … well … an upside down capital L. Part of the antenna is vertical while the rest is horizontal.

Inverted L antennas aren't normally considered to be limited space designs. In fact, they are commonly used for 80 and 160 meter operating where the horizontal portion of the antenna can exceed 100 feet in length. The reason for its popularity for low-band operating has to do with its relatively small size (compared to a 160 meter dipole at 260 feet!) and the fact that its radiation pattern combines vertically and horizontally polarized fields, giving the antenna a bit of an edge under dicey propagation conditions.

A few years ago, *QST* Technical Editor Joel Hallas, W1ZR, and I were

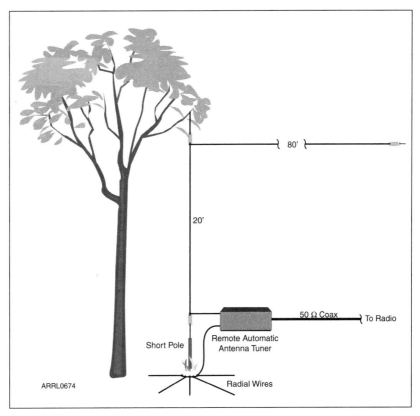

Figure 1.22 — An Inverted L antenna can be fed with a remote automatic antenna tuner at its base.

discussing antenna options for my tiny swatch of property. Noting that I had two trees available, Joel suggested a short Inverted L with a remote automatic antenna tuner at the base (**Figure 1.22**).

The result was an antenna with a 20-foot vertical section and an 80 foot horizontal portion that stretched over the top of the house to a pine tree on the corner of the lot. An MFJ-927 remote automatic antenna tuner was housed in a plastic weatherproof box at the base of the vertical section. The vertical wire attached to the tuner's "long wire" connection. I laid 20 radial wires on the ground, each about 30 feet in length, and attached them to the ground side of the tuner.

My Inverted L was more than a ½ wavelength on 40 meters, but shorter than ½ wavelength on 80 meters. Perhaps that was the "magic" length for my installation, one that provided an impedance on every band that was well

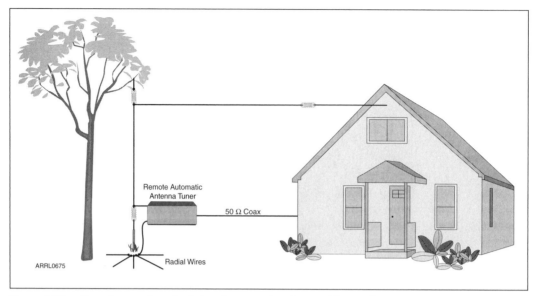

Figure 1.23 — If you have only a single tree to support an Inverted L, your house can function as the support for the "far" end.

within the range of the MFJ tuner. Regardless, the tuner was able to find an acceptable match on all bands from 10 through 160 meters. Of course, on 160 meters the antenna was quite short, but I was still able to make contact with stations 500 miles distant running just 100 W on CW. The performance on 40 meters and up was impressive and seemed to rival the all-band dipole arrangement I had been using previously.

If you have two supports available, a short Inverted L with a remote tuner might be an option to consider. Even if you have just a single tree, it may be possible to use your house as the support for the far end of the horizontal section (see **Figure 1.23**). Don't worry too much about the dimensions. As with most wire antennas the axiom "high as possible and long as possible" applies. Make the vertical section as high as you can get it and the horizontal section as long as your space allows. Also put down as many radials as feasible and make them as long as possible. As you'll learn when we discuss vertical antennas, recent research has shown that you don't need a huge network of radials for acceptable performance. If all you can do is install just a handful of radials, so be it. You'll likely find that the remote tuner will still find matches on several bands and the antenna will perform in ways that will surprise you.

End-Fed Wire Antennas

End-fed wire antennas have an ancient pedigree going all the way back to the beginning of Amateur Radio itself. They remain in the ham radio antenna arsenal today because they are relatively easy to set up and use in almost any environment. For best performance they require one high support, a ground return system of some sort (radials or a counterpoise wire) and an impedance matching network, typically an antenna tuner.

For amateurs with space limitations, an end-fed wire may offer an attractive solution. For example, I've had good luck using a 70-foot end-fed wire and an Icom AH-4 remote automatic antenna tuner (see **Figure 1.24**). My automatic tuner was attached to the back of a utility shed. The antenna ran from the branch of a tall oak tree (the branch was about 40 feet from the ground) to the side of the shed. A short wire dropped down to the antenna tuner, connecting to the "hot" terminal on the AH-4. The ground terminal was connected to a network of 20 buried radial wires, each about 40 feet long. With this setup I managed to make a "Clean Sweep" (working all US and Canadian sections) during the 2003 ARRL Phone Sweepstakes contest. Not too shabby for an antenna tuner and a collection of wire.

There was nothing magical about the 70-foot length of my antenna. With an end-fed wire longer is always better, but if you can only string up,

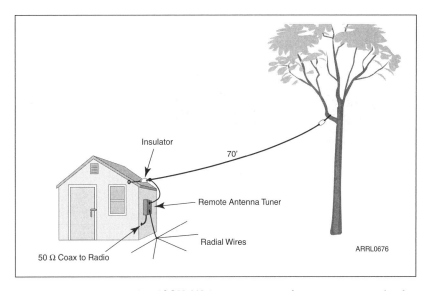

Figure 1.24 — I once used an ICOM AH-4 remote automatic antenna tuner to load an end-fed wire. The wire sloped down from a tree to the tuner, which was mounted on the exterior wall of a shed. The tuner ground was connected to a network of 10 30-foot radial wires. The antenna worked remarkably well from 160 through 10 meters.

Figure 1.25 — The DX Engineering offers a commercial version of the end-fed wire configuration depicted in Figure 1.23. Their DXE-SMBA-2 package includes a remote automatic antenna tuner in a watertight enclosure. This very low profile unit is easily hidden — even in small bushes or shrubs — and the only thing that shows is the wire antenna element which can be a very small diameter for a near-zero visual impact. [Photo courtesy of DX Engineering]

say, 45 feet of wire, you can be reasonably sure it will work on 80 through 10 meters. There is also nothing magical about the ICOM AH-4 antenna tuner. Any good quality tuner will do.

There is a commercial version of this concept available from DX Engineering. At the heart of their DXE-SMBA-2 package (**Figure 1.25**) is a remote automatic antenna tuner in a watertight enclosure. This very low profile unit is easily hidden — even in small bushes or shrubs — and the only thing that shows is the wire antenna element which can be a very small diameter for a near-zero visual impact. The system sells for $399 and comes complete with the tuner, stainless steel radial plate, radial wires, hardware, and even the antenna wire and two insulators.

An end-fed wire can also be a solution for condo and apartment dwellers. See **Figure 1.26**. The "station end" of the wire can attach to a windowsill while the other end is anchored in a tree. To match the wire you'll need an antenna tuner, either manual or automatic. Among manual tuner designs, look for a model that offers a balanced output in addition to its unbalanced outputs. The balanced output typically sports two binding posts that are connected to an internal 4:1 balun. The "hot" post may be red and labeled as the "long wire" connection. Your end-fed wire attaches to this post.

To the other post you'll need to attach a counterpoise wire that is ¼ wavelength at the lowest frequency you intend to use. For 40 meters, for instance, this would be about 33 feet. This may sound like a lot of wire, but you can run it along the baseboards and behind furniture; it doesn't have to be out in the open. This counterpoise may carry high voltages at times so it must be insulated, and be sure to tape the end where the conductor may be exposed.

The problem with using an end-fed wire in this fashion, as you may have guessed, is that you run the risk of introducing a lot of RF into your living environment. If you are generating significant RF power, you can easily end up with "hot" station equipment — complete with sparks and painful "bites." With that in mind, I'd recommend an installation like this only for low power operating at 10 W or less.

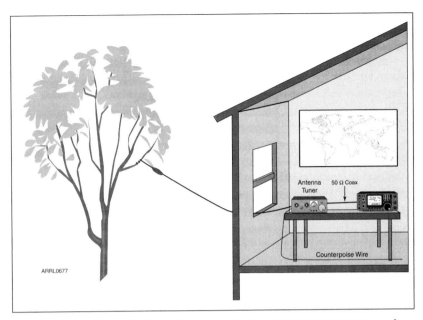

Figure 1.26 — An end-fed wire antenna can also be used by apartment or condo dwellers. The trick, however, is keeping the RF out of your equipment. To help prevent this, you'll need to attach an insulated counterpoise wire that is ¼ wavelength at your lowest frequency. The wire can be laid on the floor along the baseboards and tucked behind furniture. Considering the RF voltage and exposure issues, it is best to use low power with an antenna of this type.

Figure 1.27 -- The MFJ-931 "Artificial Ground" by MFJ Enterprises "tunes" the counterpoise wire in end-fed installations. The MFJ-931 connects between the antenna tuner ground and the counterpoise wire.

You may want to consider a device such as the MFJ-931 "Artificial Ground" manufactured by MFJ Enterprises to essentially "tune" the counterpoise wire. The MFJ-931 (**Figure 1.27**) connects between the antenna tuner ground and the counterpoise wire. By adjusting the unit you can maximize the RF current in the counterpoise and keep it from flowing in the rest of your equipment. You'll also increase the efficiency of your antenna system. When this book went to press, the MFJ-931 was selling for about $110.

Loop Antennas

The smallest size of a "large" loop is usually one having a conductor length of ½ wavelength. At 40 meters, for example, that would be 66 feet. The conductor is usually formed into a square, as shown in **Figure 1.28**, making each side ⅛ wavelength long. So for our 40-meter square loop example, each side would be 16½ feet in length. When fed at the center of one side, the current flows in a closed loop. The current distribution is approximately the same as on a ½ wavelength wire, and so is maximum at the center of the side *opposite* the feed point, and minimum at the feed point itself. This current distribution causes the field strength to be at maximum in the plane of the loop and in the direction looking from the low-current side to the high-current side.

If your property is blessed with two sizeable trees, a ½ wavelength loop could become part of your antenna farm. Looking back at our 40 meter loop again, such a square antenna could easily fit between two trees about 20 feet apart.

Stepping up in size, you have the *full wave loop*. At 40 meters you'd be talking about a total conductor length on the order of 132 feet. That translates to a square with 33-foot sides.

The directional characteristics of loops of this type in the vertical plane are opposite in sense to those of a small loop. That is, the radiation is maximum perpendicular to the plane of the loop and is at minimum in either direction in the plane containing the loop.

A loop antenna doesn't have to be formed into a square. It can be a circle or a triangle (the venerable *delta loop*). The shape of the loop *will* change its radiation pattern, as will its height above ground and the presence of nearby objects. Even so, in a cramped antenna environment we generally don't care about radiation patterns all that much. We want an antenna that *works*, and if you're looking for something that offers a slight overall performance advantage, a loop is something to consider.

Many hams prefer to feed loop antennas with 450-Ω ladder line and, of course, an antenna tuner. This is a good solution since it

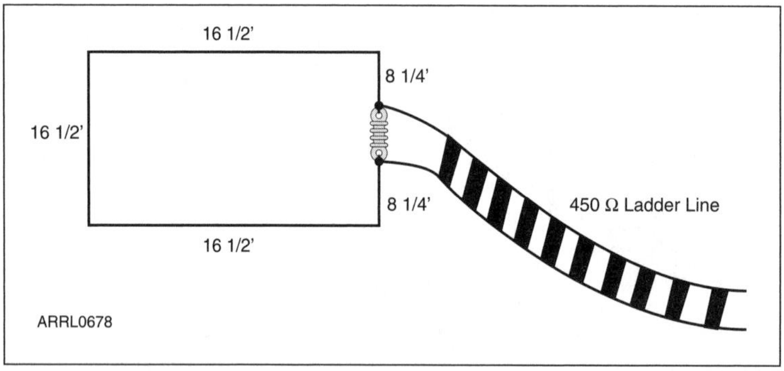

Figure 1.28 — A half-wavelength loop antenna. This one is designed for the 40 meter band.

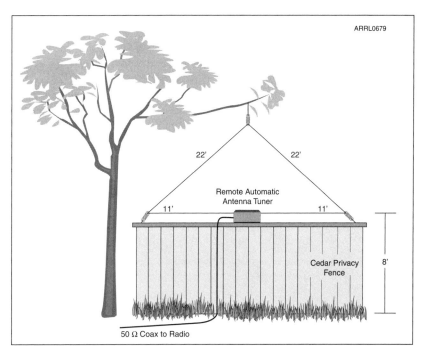

ARRL0679

22'   22'

Remote Automatic
Antenna Tuner

11'   11'

Cedar Privacy
Fence   8'

50 Ω Coax to Radio

Figure 1.29 — My "stealthy delta" loop took advantage of a cedar privacy fence and a nearby tree. The remote automatic antenna tuner loaded this antenna from 40 through 10 meters.

provides multiband operation and removes the need to tweak the loop to bring it into resonance.

I enjoyed good performance with a delta loop supported by a single tree (see **Figure 1.29**). The lower corners of the triangle were anchored atop an 8-foot tall wood privacy fence. A remote automatic antenna tuner was connected directly to the loop at one corner.

Another interesting approach that some amateurs use is to "wrap" the loop antenna around their homes using insulated wire and anchoring the corners to their gutters or roofs and feeding the antennas with 450 Ω ladder line. While a loop installation of this type is certainly stealthy (almost invisible), the home is obviously bathed in RF. Depending on the amount of power one is using, this raises RF exposure issues as well as a strong possibility of interference to every piece of electronics in the house.

Directional Antennas

The most powerful antenna for the HF bands is the directional antenna, often referred to as the *beam* antenna.

When hams speak of beam antennas, they usually mean the venerable *Yagi* and *quad* designs, with Yagis being the most common. These antennas focus your signal in a particular direction (like a flashlight). Not only do they

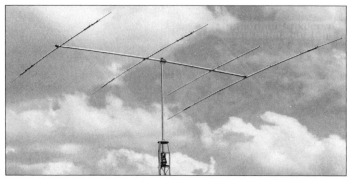

A typical tri-band Yagi antenna — one of the most popular HF directional antenna designs.

Installing a tower and a Yagi antenna is a serious undertaking. [Photo by K5EMI]

concentrate your transmitted signal, they allow you to focus your receive pattern as well. For example, if your beam is aimed west you won't hear many signals from the east (off the "back" of the beam).

The problems with beam antenna systems are size and cost. Beams for the lower HF bands are *big* antennas. At about 43 feet in width, the longest element of a 40-meter coil-loaded Yagi is wider than the wingspan of a Piper Cherokee airplane.

In terms of cost, a sizeable beam antenna and a 50-foot tower will set you back at least $2500. Then add about $500 for the antenna rotator, an electric motor that allows you to turn the antenna by remote control. On top of that, add the cost of cables, contractor fees (to plant the tower in the ground), and so on. In the end, you'll rack up about $5000, if not substantially more.

If you have that much cash burning a hole in your pocket, by all means throw it at a beam antenna and tower. The rewards will be tremendous and you'll never regret the investment. Between the signal-concentrating ability of the beam and the height advantage of the tower, you'll have the world at your fingertips. Even a beam antenna mounted on a roof tripod can make your signal an RF juggernaut.

While it is certainly possible to build your own Yagi or quad beam for your HF station, unless you have experience and good mechanical skills, I'd recommend purchasing a commercial antenna instead. See the advertising pages of *QST* magazine and you'll find many different models available from manufacturers and dealers. Among the most popular are the triple-band models commonly known as *tribanders*. These antennas offer performance on bands such as 20, 15, and 10 meters with a single feed line running back to your station.

Whether you buy or build, installing an HF beam antenna and rotator is not for the faint of heart. It can require the better part of a day to accomplish, not to mention the assistance of several individuals.

Tower installation can be even more challenging and time consuming. Erecting even a short tower (a 30-footer, for example), is a task that requires special knowledge and experience; it isn't as simple as digging a hole, dropping in the tower base and pouring concrete. There are many things to consider, such as structural integrity and electrical safety. Depending on where you live, you may also have to navigate the process of acquiring a building permit and safety inspection. If you think a tower is in your future, pick up a copy of *Antenna Towers for Radio Amateurs* by Don Daso, K4ZA, at the ARRL Store at **www.arrl.org/shop**. This is an excellent guide for every step of the process.

It isn't my intention to dissuade you from buying a big Yagi antenna and hauling it to the top of a tower. On the contrary, if you have the funds and the time, you won't find a better antenna system for your HF station. With your tower-mounted Yagi, you'll easily work stations that other hams in your area can't even hear.

For most amateurs, a beam antenna on a tower is the ultimate dream. If you have the resources to achieve it, by all means do so!

Indoor Antennas

Outdoor antennas are almost always superior to indoor designs because they are blessed with not having to push and pull signals through various types of building materials. Outdoor antennas are also further away from sources of interference (read: computers and other consumer electronics) and less likely to cause interference to those devices.

But sometimes outdoor antennas are simply impossible. You may have a landlord or condo association blocking your every move. Or you may not have enough open property to erect an antenna of any kind. Either way, your only remaining option is to head indoors.

Let's start with wire. The nice thing about wire is that you can bend and shape it to fit your requirements. Even the smallest indoor rooms can accommodate an HF wire antenna if you are willing to be creative.

The easiest indoor wire antenna is the *dipole* — a center insulator (where the feed line attaches) and two wires of equal length. If you care about operating on only one band, you can try a single-band half wavelength design. The classic formula to determine its length is:

$$468 / \text{Frequency (MHz)}$$

Into the Attic

If you're fortunate enough to live in a home, apartment, or condominium that has an attic space, you may find that you have an excellent location for an antenna farm right over your head!

Attics in modern homes tend to be rather small. Count yourself lucky if you have an attic that will allow you to stand upright; most modern attics offer, at most, 4 or 5 feet of headroom between the attic floor and the peak of the roof. Attics in newer homes also tend to be unfinished. This means that instead of a floor you will find only lumber joists packed with insulation.

The truly lucky hams are the ones who live in older homes with large finished attics. Some of these old attics are rooms unto themselves with high ceilings, finished floors and plenty of horizontal space. Hams with attics like these have room not only for wire antennas, but also even for small directional arrays.

If you live in an apartment or condominium and you're on the top floor, it's time to do some detective work. Access to the attic is typically provided by a small door, a hatchway really, that you'll find tucked away in closet or utility room. In many instances, however, these attics are shared, which means that you don't have the attic all to yourself. Approach this type of attic with special care. If you're considering the idea of stringing a wire antenna along the length of the attic, keep in mind that you'll be walking right over your neighbor's rooms as you are putting it up. They aren't likely to appreciate this and there

Jeff Blaine, AC0C, is the master of attic antennas for the HF bands, such as this one for 20 meters.

is always the danger that your foot may slip off a joist, smash through the drywall and appear in their home as an uninvited guest. It is one thing to slip and punch a hole through your own ceiling; some handiwork with a drywall patch will set it right. Your neighbor won't be nearly as understanding!

However, this formula was created with outdoor antennas in mind. It doesn't take nearby wood, drywall, electrical wiring, or heating ducts into account. You can use the formula to get into the ballpark, but count on having to lengthen or shorten the wires considerably as you tweak the antenna for the lowest SWR.

Unless you live in a mansion with enormous rooms, some folding of the dipole will be necessary. The final shape of the antenna will depend on

But having said all that, a shared attic is still an excellent place for an antenna. At the very least you could install a commercial antenna such a Bilal Isotron, a remotely adjustable mobile antenna (in a horizontal orientation, perhaps) or even a magnetic loop antenna (assuming you can get it through the hatch and into the attic). Of course, a long wire antenna is still possible in a shared attic if you are careful and considerate.

Before you start planting antennas in your attic, take a look around. Check the underside of the roof in particular. Is the underside packed with insulation? If the answer is "yes," gently pull down a small corner of the insulating material and see what is on the other side. Some types of insulation have a metal backing and, for obvious reasons, this is not a good situation for antennas. You may decide to remove such insulation, but it may have a strong negative impact on your utility bills. And if you're a renter, your landlord may be displeased if he or she finds out.

It pays to take a glance at your roof from the outside as well. You don't have to scale a ladder, but take a good look from ground level and see if you can determine whether the roof is overlaid with asphalt shingles or something similar. If your attic space is under a metal roof, that's bad news since it renders your attic unusable as an antenna farm.

Assuming that you can use your attic, what's the best antenna to put up there? The answer is easy: largest antenna that will fit the space. Even if you have a relatively small attic chances are good that you can install the same wire dipole or loop that you would use

indoors. For example, I have used remote automatic antenna tuners in attics with good success. In one townhouse attic I installed a small wire loop antenna in the 20 foot by 20 foot attic, stringing the wires along the rafters and holding them in place with nylon string. At the feed point I ran a 6 foot length of ladder line to a remote automatic antenna tuner. From the antenna tuner I snaked 30 feet of RG-58 coaxial cable all the way back to my radio. With this arrangement I was able to operate on 30 through 10 meters.

Depending on the size and the design of your attic, you can do some amazingly creative things. For instance, let's say that you have a sizable attic in a house with wood or vinyl siding. It is possible to use such an attic to install a wire Yagi antenna for 20 meters or the higher bands by draping wires for the antenna element along the rafters. To be sure, this would be a challenging antenna design. You would have to do quite a bit of trimming and repositioning of wires to finally achieve the best result. And it goes without saying that this antenna would have a fixed pattern since you wouldn't be able to rotate it. Even so, a large directional antenna can be built within an attic and it will work quite well. I once installed an antenna like this for the 10 meter band while I was living in a condominium with a relatively small attic. It took me all day, even with an antenna analyzer, to finally get all the wires in the right places and the antenna adjusted for the lowest SWR, but DX stations within the pattern of my antenna reported that I often had a booming signal while running just 100 W.

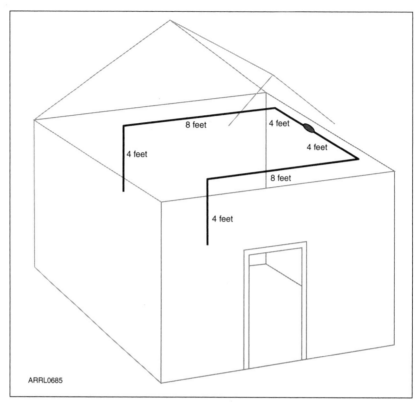

8 feet

4 feet

4 feet

4 feet

8 feet

4 feet

ARRL0685

Figure 1.30 – Even a dipole antenna for the 20 meter band can fit into a small room with a bit of folding.

the dimensions and configuration of the room. The center of the dipole carries the most current and therefore does most of the radiating, so this part should be as high and unfolded as possible. Because the ends of the dipole radiate less energy than the center, their orientation is not as important. They do carry the maximum voltage, however, so care should be taken to position the ends far enough from other conductors to avoid arcing, or contact with people or animals.

The dipole may end up being L-shaped, Z-shaped, U-shaped or some indescribable corkscrew shape, depending on what space is available. As an example, consider the 20-meter dipole shown in **Figure 1.30**. Using the formula, we find that each leg is about 16 feet in length, yet it can squeeze into a small 10 × 10 foot bedroom with some creative folding.

I used an antenna like this to work many stations from a two story apartment while running about 25 W output (mostly CW at the time). To keep my wife happy, I made the dipole out of ordinary two-conductor speaker wire

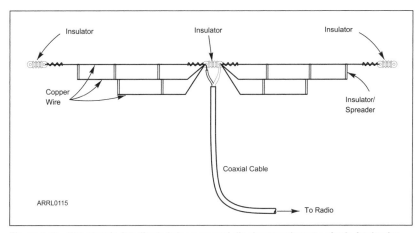

Figure 1.31 – The classic fan dipole brings several dipoles together at a single feed point.

that I painted white to match the walls and ceiling. White thumbtacks held the wires along the corners where the walls met the ceiling. I even painted the coaxial feed line white to help camouflage it against the drywall. An alternative to consider, if you are running low power, is flat wire adhesive tape. It comes in large rolls and is easy to stick to a wall.

The most difficult aspect of setting up a single-band resonant dipole is trimming it for lowest SWR. You have to add or subtract wire in equal lengths from each leg of the antenna while taking SWR measurements to observe the results. On the other hand, one of the great things about indoor wire antennas is that they are easy to adjust — no need to climb ladders or brave inclement weather.

What if you want to operate on more than one band with your wire antenna? One approach is a variation on the venerable *fan dipole* that amounts to two or more dipoles attached to the same feed point (see **Figure 1.31**). When used outdoors, a fan dipole can present a challenge because the individual wire dipoles tend to interact, making adjustment an exercise in frustration. One way to reduce interaction is to have the dipoles arranged at right angles to each other.

Indoors, separating the dipoles can be a difficult proposition, but not impossible. **Figure 1.32** illustrates a design that makes the best use of two rooms. In this example, the 20 meter dipole is installed and folded into one room. The 15-meter dipole attaches to the same feed point, but extends into adjacent living room (more small wires and white paint).

The easiest way to get multiband performance from a wire dipole antenna is to use an antenna tuner. See **Figure 1.33**. Here we have a

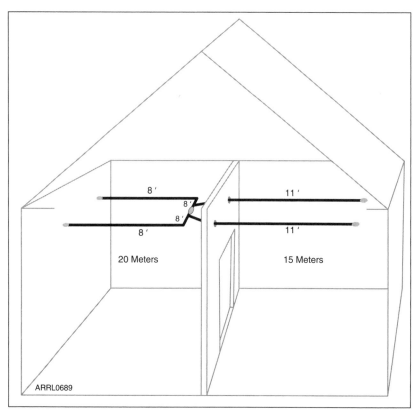

8 '

8 '

8 '

11 '

8 '

11 '

20 Meters

15 Meters

ARRL0689

Figure 1.32 — In this example we have a 20 meter dipole in one room and a 15 meter dipole in an adjoining room — both connected at the same feed point.

20-meter dipole along the ceiling, but notice that it is being fed with 450 Ω windowed *ladder line* rather than coaxial cable. Instead of the feed line snaking all the way back to the transceiver, it connects to the antenna tuner instead (a tuner with a balanced output port). The tuner, in turn, connects to the transceiver. You can use a setup like this to operate on any frequency at which the antenna tuner can provide a sufficiently low SWR for your radio. Since you are using a short length of ladder line, the losses between the tuner and the antenna caused by high SWR are almost irrelevant.

If you want to have your radio in a separate room, but don't want to run bulky, highly visible ladder line through your home, look at the alternative in **Figure 1.34**. The antenna tuner can reside in a discreet location near the antenna, but thin coax such as RG-58 can make the rest of the journey back to the transceiver.

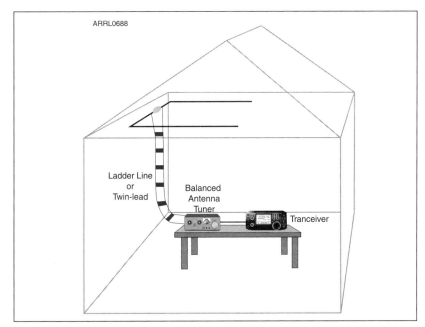

Figure 1.33 — A multiband ceiling dipole fed with 450-Ω ladder line. Unlike a tuned dipole, the length isn't critical. As a rule of thumb, make each leg of the dipole as long as the space allows and make sure both legs are of equal lengths.

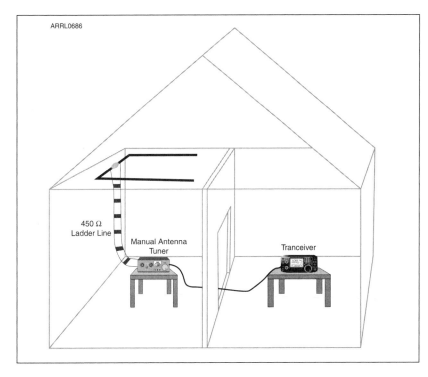

Figure 1.34 — If your station and your multiband antenna are in separate rooms, consider placing the manual antenna tuner close to the antenna, feeding the antenna with 450-Ω ladder line and then using thin RG-58 coaxial cable between the tuner and the radio.

The configuration in Figure 1.34 is not ideal. Every time you change frequency at the transceiver, you'll probably have to go into the other room and adjust the antenna tuner. You can mark the positions of the tuner knobs to make this somewhat easier, but it is still an annoyance. The solution is to use a remote automatic antenna tuner. Depending on the type of automatic tuner you purchase, all you have to do is send a switching command from your radio or simply begin transmitting. The tuner will automatically seek the best SWR and you won't have to move a muscle. Automatic tuners are not cheap. They typically cost $200 to $400. Even so, the sheer convenience is well worth the price.

So far we've been talking about dipoles, but that isn't the only option for wire antennas inside your home. Another option to consider is the *loop* antenna.

A loop antenna is exactly as it appears to be. It is a loop of wire connected to the feed line, which must seem pretty strange at first glance. Looking at a loop antenna, it appears to be a dead short, electrically speaking. But on the contrary, when RF is applied to a loop of wire, it sees that wire not as a dead short, but as a load with a specific impedance. When you consider

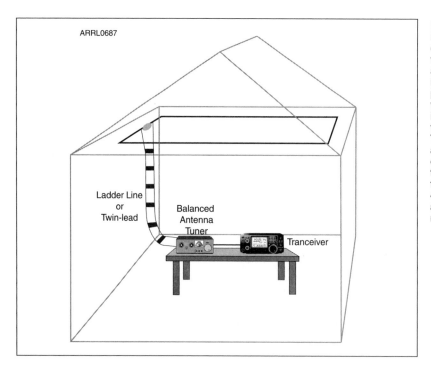

Figure 1.35 – A loop antenna is a continuous circle of wire that attaches at either side of an insulator at the feed point. In this example we have a loop installed within a room, typically on the ceiling. The loop should be as large as the room can accommodate. In this example, we're feeding the loop with 450-Ω ladder line and an antenna tuner for multiband operation.

an ordinary room, you can see that there are many opportunities for loop antennas. Take a look at **Figure 1.35** for just one example. In this example, the loop wire travels along the edge of the entire ceiling, connecting to a short length of 450 Ω windowed line that attaches to an antenna tuner. This is the same type of balanced antenna tuner we discussed before. Despite the relatively small diameter of this loop, an antenna tuner with a wide tuning range should be able to find a match on several different bands. This same loop antenna could just as easily be installed vertically on the wall; it all depends on the layout of your house or apartment. As with all antennas, higher is always better. If you live in a structure with aluminum siding, attaching the loop antenna to the ceiling rather than the wall is the best choice.

Although we've been talking about making your own indoor antennas, you can just as easily use commercial antennas indoors as well. In fact, as long as the antenna is small enough to fit inside the room of your choice, any antenna can be used.

One idea to consider is a mobile antenna. Even though these antennas are designed for use on cars, they can function just as well without being attached to a vehicle. The difference is that instead of a car body acting as a ground plane, you must use radial wires or perhaps a single wire known as a *counterpoise* attached to the ground point of the antenna. Some mobile antenna manufacturers have anticipated that their products would be used this way and they've provided supports such as tripods to make this possible. The Sidekick by High Sierra is a typical example of a mobile antenna that can be attached to a tripod and used indoors in a room with sufficiently high ceilings (9 to 10 feet).

Depending on the mobile antenna design, you may need to adjust a tap or coil whenever you wish to change bands. However, other mobile antennas use motorized mechanical adjustments that can even be performed remotely using a small control box that you would keep by your radio.

It is interesting to note that you can also take two single-band mobile antennas and use them together as a dipole antenna. Manufacturers such as MFJ and High Sierra sell special mounting brackets that allow you to connect two mobile antennas together in this fashion. The mobile antennas screw into the bracket, and then you simply attach a coaxial feed line. As handy as this arrangement might be, two mobile antennas back-to-back can still make for a rather long dipole antenna. For example, two Hamstick-style mobile antennas together for the 20-meter band are approximately 14 feet in length. In addition, these antennas tend to be inefficient, lossy radiators. The 2:1 SWR bandwidth is on the order of about 150 kilohertz at best. Even so, they offer an alternative approach for indoor operating, especially if you have sizable attic space available.

There are other small antenna designs that do not require radials or any other type of ground system. One well known example is the Bilal Isotron antenna. The Isotron has been around for many years. Without oversimplifying, the Isotron is an extremely compact design comprised of a loading coil and metal plates (depending on the model). The Isotron can be placed on a short mast and set up just about anywhere in a room. Depending on how much power you're running, it is best to keep the Isotron well away from nearby objects and people. High voltages can develop and they could be hazardous, not to mention the RF exposure concerns.

Yet another antenna to consider for use indoors is a so-called *magnetic loop*. The antenna itself is not magnetic in any way. When used as a receiving antenna, however, it's said that the antenna primarily responds to the magnetic component of the received signal. Magnetic loop antennas have been around for decades and are popular mainly because there are highly portable. During WWII and even throughout the Vietnam War era, the military used magnetic loop antennas for this very reason. Compared to a dipole antenna, a magnetic loop antenna is not a very efficient radiator, but it can be effective when tuned properly. Perhaps the most popular commercially available loop is the MFJ-1788 Super Hi-Q loop. This magnetic loop is only about 4 feet in diameter, yet it can operate on every band from 30 through

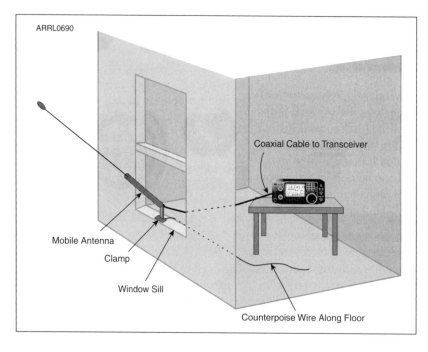

ARRL0690

Coaxial Cable to Transceiver

Mobile Antenna

Clamp

Window Sill

Counterpoise Wire Along Floor

Figure 1.36 — A mobile antenna can clamp to a windowsill and extend outdoors. To provide an RF current "return," a counterpoise wire attaches to the antenna ground point (where it would normally attach to a car body). This wire should be at least ¼ wavelength at the desired frequency if the mobile antenna is a single-band design. If it is a multiband tunable antenna, the counterpoise should be ¼ wavelength at the lowest frequency you intend to use.

Figure 1.37 — The Super Antennas MP-1 is a multiband HF antenna intended for portable operating. However, it can also be used indoors.

10 meters. The antenna has a built-in tuning mechanism consisting of a large variable capacitor attached to an electric motor. By operating the motor by remote control you can adjust the antenna for the lowest SWR. Like the Isotron, the MFJ loop does not require a ground system or radial wires. It does pose the same voltage and RF exposure concerns.

Speaking of tuning, it is important to note that small antennas tend to have very narrow 2:1 SWR bandwidths. Magnetic loop antennas in particular can have extremely narrow bandwidths on the order of just a few kHz. You may find that you must frequently re-tune whenever you change frequency.

The type of indoor antenna you choose, of course, depends on your circumstances and the size of your wallet. Wire antennas are obviously the least expensive, but for easy multiband operation you may have to also invest in an antenna tuner. Yes, some transceivers have built-in tuners, but most of these do not have the impedance range necessary for the task.

And wire antennas don't lend themselves to being easily put up or taken down at a moment's notice. When you install a wire antenna in a room, you do it with the expectation that it is going to be there for a long time, hence the need to camouflage it –unless you have a very understanding spouse. Smaller freestanding antennas such as mobile antennas, the Bilal Isotron, or the MFJ loop are much easier to set up or put away as required, but they may be more expensive than a simple do-it-yourself antenna.

As you are examining your indoor antenna options, don't forget your windows. Depending on how strict your landlord or homeowner association may be, it is certainly possible to mount a mobile antenna on a windowsill with the radiating portion outside the window and the radials or counterpoise wire inside the room. See **Figure 1.36**. You will also find a number of HF portable antennas designed for low power outdoor operating that can also serve indoors or as window antennas. These antennas may be too tall to fit inside the average room, but they can certainly be mounted on a windowsill. Take a look at **Figure 1.37**. This is the model MP-1 portable HF antenna manufactured by Super Antennas. The MP-1 comes with a mounting bracket and clamp that are ideal for use in a window mounting situation. To change bands you simply move the metal sleeve up and down the loading coil. The MP-1 can also be removed quickly if necessary.

MFJ Enterprises offers an antenna known as the MFJ-1622 that is specifically designed for apartment window installations. The mount attaches to the window and the antenna is adjusted for the lowest SWR by selecting coil taps. See **Figure 1.38**.

Once again, none of these very small HF antennas are particularly efficient, but when used with a narrow bandwidth mode such as CW or PSK 31, they will provide hours of enjoyment.

Your Feed Line: the Critical Link

Feed lines are the unsung heroes of antenna systems. Unlike antennas, they aren't physically attractive. You don't usually see hams gazing in rapturous awe at feed lines. To most of us, feed lines are simply the cables that transport signals to and from our antennas. We may not give them much consideration, but that would be a grave mistake.

Coaxial Cable

At the most basic level, coaxial cable, or simply "coax" for short, consists of one conductor — the *center conductor* — surrounded by another — the *shield* — and separated by some sort of insulating material. In the types of coax hams most often encounter, the insulating material is either solid or foam plastic of one type or another, or it may be an open space filled with ordinary air.

The type of insulating material used, the composition of the shield (solid metal or wire mesh or both) and the distance separating the center conductor from the shield are major factors in determining the overall *characteristics* of a given type of coax. We use the word "characteristics" to mean all the various factors that determine how coaxial cable behaves when RF energy is applied to it. There are a number of different characteristics, but the most important ones for our discussion are the characteristic impedance of the cable in ohms (Ω) and the degree of loss you can expect over a certain length.

If you look at **Table 1.1** you'll see a list of many types of coaxial cable along with their primary characteristics. Pay particular attention to the four right hand columns that list "Matched Loss" in "dB per 100 feet." This is a measure of how much RF — both transmitted *and received* — you will lose in 100 feet of cable. The individual columns are labeled according to the frequency in question: 1, 10, 100, and 1000 MHz. The loss specification assumes that the impedance of the cable — usually 50 Ω -- is perfectly matched to a 50 Ω load (the antenna). If it isn't, all bets are off, but we'll address that situation in a moment. For now, assume that the cable is connected to an ideal 50 Ω load.

As you examine the table carefully, you'll notice some interesting things:

❑ **Loss varies quite a bit depending on the type of cable you are using.** RG174, for example, is a thin variety of coax that's great for short connections inside pieces of equipment, but it absorbs RF energy like a sponge when the length goes beyond several feet, depending on the frequency (see below). At the opposite extreme you have Hardline, the lowest loss coaxial feed line available. Hardline is great stuff, but it is expensive and difficult to work with. The only time you usually find hams using Hardline is when they need to feed antennas that are considerable distances from their transceivers.

❑ **Loss increases with frequency.** This is an inviolate rule of feed lines. The higher the frequency, the greater the loss. A few comparisons will demonstrate this fact.

Let's say you are feeding a 50 Ω antenna with 100 feet of RG-58 coax and transmitting at 14 MHz. That calculates to a loss of 1.33 dB. So, if you have 100 W at your transceiver, you'll end up with about 74 W at the antenna.

Now let's ramp up the frequency to 144 MHz and leave everything else the same. The loss skyrockets to 4.6 dB. Of the 100 W at the transmitter, only 35 W is arriving at the antenna! All the rest is being dissipated as heat along the length of the cable.

As you can see, when choosing coax one must choose wisely. If your antenna is fewer than 100 feet from your station and you're operating at HF frequencies, you can get away with something inexpensive such as RG-58. There will always be a certain amount of loss, but it will be so small as to be unimportant in the greater scheme of things. Remember, however, that loss increases with frequency. The loss in 100 feet of RG-58 when operating at 3.5 MHz meters may be negligible, but jump to the 10 meter band and it becomes significant.

Low loss coaxial cable is more expensive, but definitely worth the investment.

Table 1.1

Nominal Characteristics of Commonly Used Transmission Lines

RG or Type	Part Number	Nom. Z_0 Ω	VF %	Cap. pF/ft	Cent. Cond. AWG	Diel. Type	Shield Type	Jacket Matl	OD inches	Max V (RMS)	1 MHz	Matched Loss (dB/100') 10	100	1000
RG-6	Belden 1694A	75	82	16.2	#18 Solid BC	FPE	FC	P1	0.275	600	0.2	.7	1.8	5.9
RG-6	Belden 8215	75	66	20.5	#21 Solid CCS	PE	D	PE	0.332	2700	0.4	0.8	2.7	9.8
RG-8	Belden 7810A	50	86	23.0	#10 Solid BC	FPE	FC	PE	0.405	600	0.1	0.4	1.2	4.0
RG-8	TMS LMR400	50	85	23.9	#10 Solid CCA	FPE	FC	PE	0.405	600	0.1	0.4	1.3	4.1
RG-8	Belden 9913	50	84	24.6	#10 Solid BC	ASPE	FC	P1	0.405	600	0.1	0.4	1.3	4.5
RG-8	CXP1318FX	50	84	24.0	#10 Flex BC	FPE	FC	P2N	0.405	600	0.1	0.4	1.3	4.5
RG-8	Belden 9913F7	50	83	24.6	#11 Flex BC	FPE	FC	P1	0.405	600	0.2	0.6	1.5	4.8
RG-8	Belden 9914	50	82	24.8	#10 Solid BC	FPE	FC	P1	0.405	600	0.2	0.6	1.5	4.8
RG-8	TMS LMR400UF	50	85	23.9	#10 Flex BC	FPE	FC	PE	0.405	600	0.1	0.4	1.4	4.8
RG-8	DRF-BF	50	84	24.5	#9.5 Flex BC	FPE	FC	PE	0.405	600	0.1	0.5	1.6	4.9
RG-8	WM CQ106	50	84	24.5	#9.5 Flex BC	FPE	FC	P2N	0.405	600	0.2	0.6	1.6	5.2
RG-8	CXP008	50	78	26.0	#13 Flex BC	FPE	FC	P1	0.405	600	0.1	0.5	1.8	7.1
RG-8	Belden 8237	52	66	29.5	#13 Flex BC	PE	S	P1	0.405	3700	0.2	0.6	1.9	7.4
RG-8X	Belden 7808A	50	86	23.5	#15 Solid BC	FPE	FC	PE	0.240	600	0.2	0.7	2.3	7.4
RG-8X	TMS LMR240	50	84	24.2	#15 Solid BC	FPE	FC	PE	0.242	300	0.2	0.8	2.5	8.0
RG-8X	WM CQ118	50	82	25.0	#16 Flex BC	FPE	FC	P2N	0.242	300	0.3	0.9	2.8	8.4
RG-8X	TMS LMR240UF	50	84	24.2	#15 Flex BC	FPE	S	PE	0.242	300	0.3	0.8	2.8	9.6
RG-8X	Belden 9258	50	82	24.8	#16 Flex BC	FPE	S	P1	0.242	600	0.3	0.9	3.1	11.2
RG-8X	CXP08XB	50	80	25.3	#16 Flex BC	FPE	S	P1	0.242	300	0.3	0.9	3.1	14.0
RG-9	Belden 8242	51	66	30.0	#13 Flex SPC	PE	SCBC	P2N	0.420	5000	0.2	0.6	2.1	8.2
RG-11	Belden 8213	75	84	16.1	#14 Solid BC	FPE	S	PE	0.405	600	0.2	0.4	1.3	5.2
RG-11	Belden 8238	75	66	20.5	#18 Flex TC	PE	S	P1	0.405	600	0.2	0.7	2.0	7.1
RG-58	Belden 7807A	50	85	23.7	#18 Solid BC	FPE	FC	PE	0.195	300	0.3	1.0	3.0	9.7
RG-58	TMS LMR200	50	83	24.5	#17 Solid BC	FPE	FC	PE	0.195	300	0.3	1.0	3.2	10.5
RG-58	WM CQ124	52	66	28.5	#20 Solid BC	PE	S	PE	0.195	1400	0.4	1.3	4.3	14.3
RG-58A	Belden 8240	52	66	28.5	#20 Solid BC	PE	S	P1	0.193	1400	0.3	1.1	3.8	14.5
RG-58A	Belden 8219	53	73	26.5	#20 Flex TC	FPE	S	P1	0.195	300	0.3	1.3	4.5	18.1
RG-58C	Belden 8262	50	66	30.8	#20 Flex TC	PE	S	P2N	0.195	1900	0.4	1.4	4.9	21.5
RG-58A	Belden 8259	50	66	30.8	#20 Flex TC	PE	S	P1	0.192	1900	0.4	1.5	5.4	22.8
RG-59	Belden 1426A	75	83	16.3	#20 Solid BC	FPE	S	P1	0.242	300	0.3	0.9	2.6	8.5
RG-59	CXP 0815	75	82	16.2	#20 Solid BC	FPE	S	P1	0.232	300	0.5	0.9	2.2	9.1
RG-59	Belden 8212	75	78	17.3	#20 Solid CCS	FPE	S	P1	0.242	300	0.6	1.0	3.0	10.9
RG-59	Belden 8241	75	66	20.4	#23 Solid CCS	PE	S	P1	0.242	1700	0.6	1.1	3.4	12.0
RG-62A	Belden 9269	93	84	13.5	#22 Solid CCS	ASPE	S	P1	0.240	750	0.3	0.9	2.7	8.7
RG-62B	Belden 8255	93	84	13.5	#24 Flex CCS	ASPE	S	P2N	0.242	750	0.3	0.9	2.9	11.0
RG-63B	Belden 9857	125	84	9.7	#22 Solid CCS	ASPE	S	P2N	0.405	750	0.2	0.5	1.5	5.8
RG-142	CXP 183242	50	69.5	29.4	#19 Solid SCCS	TFE	D	FEP	0.195	1900	0.3	1.1	3.8	12.8
RG-142B	Belden 83242	50	69.5	29.0	#19 Solid SCCS	TFE	D	TFE	0.195	1400	0.3	1.1	3.9	13.5
RG-174	Belden 7805R	50	73.5	26.2	#25 Solid BC	FPE	FC	P1	0.110	300	0.6	2.0	6.5	21.3
RG-174	Belden 8216	50	66	30.8	#26 Flex CCS	PE	S	P1	0.110	1100	1.9	3.3	8.4	34.0

Type	Cable	Center Conductor	Z (Ω)	VF (%)	pF/ft	Diel.	Shield	Jacket	OD (in)	Max V	dB	dB	dB	dB
RG-213	Belden 8267	#13 Flex BC	50	66	30.8	P2N	S	PE	0.405	3700	0.2	0.6	1.9	8.0
RG-213	CXP213	#13 Flex BC	50	66	30.8	P2N	S	PE	0.405	600	0.2	0.6	2.0	8.2
RG-214	Belden 8268	#13 Flex SPC	50	66	30.8	P2N	D	PE	0.425	3700	0.2	0.6	1.9	8.0
RG-216	Belden 9850	#18 Flex TC	75	66	20.5	P2N	D	PE	0.425	3700	0.2	0.7	2.0	7.1
RG-217	WM CQ217F	#10 Flex BC	50	66	30.8	PE	D	PE	0.545	7000	0.1	0.4	1.4	5.2
RG-217	M17/78-RG217	#10 Solid BC	50	66	30.8	PE	D	PE	0.545	7000	0.1	0.4	1.4	5.2
RG-218	M17/79-RG218	#4.5 Solid BC	50	66	29.5	P2N	S	PE	0.870	11000	0.1	0.2	0.8	3.4
RG-223	Belden 9273	#19 Solid SPC	50	66	30.8	P2N	D	PE	0.212	1400	0.4	1.2	4.1	14.5
RG-303	Belden 84303	#18 Solid SCCS	50	69.5	29.0	TFE	S	TFE	0.170	1400	0.3	1.1	3.9	13.5
RG-316	CXP TJ1316	#26 Flex BC	50	69.5	29.4	FEP	S	TFE	0.098	1200	1.2	2.7	8.0	26.1
RG-316	Belden 84316	#26 Flex SCCS	50	69.5	29.0	FEP	S	TFE	0.096	900	1.2	2.7	8.3	29.0
RG-393	M17/127-RG393	#12 Flex SPC	50	69.5	29.4	FEP	D	TFE	0.390	5000	0.2	0.5	1.7	6.1
RG-400	M17/128-RG400	#20 Flex SPC	50	69.5	29.4	FEP	D	TFE	0.195	1400	0.4	1.1	3.9	13.2
LMR500	TMS LMR500UF	#7 Flex BC	50	85	23.9	PE	FC	FPE	0.500	2500	0.1	0.4	1.2	4.0
LMR500	TMS LMR500	#7 Solid CCA	50	85	23.9	PE	FC	FPE	0.500	2500	0.1	0.3	0.9	3.3
LMR600	TMS LMR600	#5.5 Solid CCA	50	86	23.4	PE	FC	FPE	0.590	4000	0.1	0.2	0.8	2.7
LMR600	TMS LMR600UF	#5.5 Flex BC	50	86	23.4	PE	FC	FPE	0.590	4000	0.04	0.2	0.8	2.7
LMR1200	TMS LMR1200	#0 Copper Tube	50	88	23.1	PE	FC	FPE	1.200	4500		0.1	0.4	1.3
Hardline														
1/2"	CATV Hardline	#5.5 BC	50	81	25.0	none	SM	FPE	0.500	2500	0.05	0.2	0.8	3.2
1/2"	CATV Hardline	#11.5 BC	75	81	16.7	none	SM	FPE	0.500	2500	0.03	0.2	0.8	3.2
7/8"	CATV Hardline	#1 BC	50	81	25.0	none	SM	FPE	0.875	4000	0.03	0.1	0.6	2.9
7/8"	CATV Hardline	#5.5 BC	75	81	16.7	none	SM	FPE	0.875	4000		0.1	0.6	2.9
LDF4-50A	Heliax –1/2"	#5 Solid BC	50	88	25.9	PE	CC	FPE	0.630	1400	0.05	0.2	0.6	2.4
LDF5-50A	Heliax –7/8"	0.355" BC	50	88	25.9	PE	CC	FPE	1.090	2100	0.03	0.10	0.4	1.3
LDF6-50A	Heliax –1¼"	0.516" BC	50	88	25.9	PE	CC	FPE	1.550	3200	0.02	0.08	0.3	1.1

Veteran hams will say that you should always use the lowest loss coax you can afford. This is generally true — to a point. Low-loss coax often comes with a "high loss" price tag and there is most definitely a point of diminishing returns.

Let's say you have a 10 meter antenna that you are feeding with 100 feet of coaxial cable. Here is the cost breakdown vs the expected loss (in dB), assuming a matched load. The costs were current when this book was written in late 2013.

❏ RG58   Cost = $24   Loss = 2.0 dB
❏ RG8X   Cost = $29   Loss = 1.6 dB
❏ RG213   Cost = $89   Lost = 1.0 dB
❏ LMR400   Cost = $119   Loss = 0.7 dB

One hundred feet of LMR400 will cost you $119 and the loss is 0.7 dB compared to a loss of 2 dB with RG58. This may look good at first glance, but a 1.3 dB difference is not worth paying nearly five times as much. The ham at the other end of your signal path wouldn't notice the change on his S meter!

Belden RG-58 is a popular, inexpensive cable, but it can become significantly lossy on higher bands such as 10 meters.

Ladder Line

A feed line doesn't need to consist of one conductor within another. That's how coaxial cable is designed because it makes the feed line easy to work with. Since the shield entirely surrounds the center conductor, interactions with the outside environment are minimized. As a result, you can bend coax (within reason), run it across a sheet metal roof, and commit other abuses without substantially changing its impedance. That's what makes coax so popular.

But there is another type of feed line that has its roots in the early days of Amateur Radio. Back then hams often fed their antennas by simply running two wires in parallel, using insulators to keep the wires separated by a specific distance to maintain the impedance. The result was a feed line that resembled a rope ladder hanging from the antenna — *ladder line*.

We use the term "ladder line" today to mean any type of feed line comprised of two parallel wires. Traditional "true" ladder line is still available from a few vendors, but you rarely see it in use. Instead, the most popular variety is "windowed line." In windowed line the parallel conductors are separated by a plastic insulating material that features open sections every inch or so.

The advantage of ladder line over coax is its relative lack of loss. Ladder line has extraordinarily low RF loss, even at VHF frequencies, over astonishing lengths. Considering this fact, you're probably wondering why ladder line isn't used everywhere. It seems like the ideal feed line, doesn't it?

Not so fast. There are a couple of issues with ladder line that greatly diminish its utility.

❏ **Impedance.** Ladder line impedance is typically in the neighborhood of several hundred ohms. For instance, windowed line is 450 Ω and true ladder line is 600 Ω. This is a serious problem when your transceiver is designed to expect a 50 Ω coaxial feed line.

❏ **Ease of use.** Unlike coax, ladder line must be kept reasonably straight and well away from metal objects. The parallel conductors generate fields that effectively balance each other (which is why it is referred to as a "balanced line"). A sizeable chunk of metal within a few inches is sufficient to disrupt the fields, changing the characteristics of the feed line at that point. A ladder line encased in ice or snow will also change its characteristics for the same reason.

These shortcomings notwithstanding, ladder line remains attractive for amateur use, so long as you can work within the restrictions. As you'll see elsewhere in this book, one of the most efficient multiband HF antennas you can build is fed with ladder line.

SWR — The Joker in the Deck

No discussion of feed lines is complete without introducing the concept of *Standing Wave Ratio*, or SWR. Entire books have been devoted to the subject of SWR and feed lines, so I won't go into great detail here. Instead, try this bit of visualization.

Imagine a small pond with a vibrating motor in the center, just at the surface of the water. There is nothing special about the motor; all it does is vibrate. When you start the motor, its vibrations cause ripples to radiate outward in all directions. The ripples strike the soil along the edge of the pond and bounce backward in the general direction of the motor. These reflected ripples collide with the "new" ripples being generated by the motor. As they collide they add or subtract from one another. The motor keeps vibrating and these wave interactions continue.

As we stand on the shore and observe, we see the first ripples striking the pond edge and returning, but within seconds it is apparent that we can no longer see moving ripples at all. Instead, we see what appears to be a fixed, non-moving pattern of waves on the surface of the pond. All the traveling waves have collided and merged into a series of *standing waves*. These standing waves will remain in place so long as nothing changes, including the vibrating frequency of the motor.

Now substitute RF waves in a feed line for water, a transceiver for the motor, and an antenna for the edge of the pond. The energy your transceiver sends into the feed line, the *forward power*, travels to the antenna. Some of the energy is radiated, but a portion is reflected. This *reflected power* goes racing back down the feed line toward the transceiver where it will ultimately bounce back to the antenna. Along the way it encounters forward power from the transceiver. Just like our pond analogy, the waves of energy interact, adding and subtracting. The result is standing waves on the feed line.

Some amateurs believe that SWR is a simple ratio of forward to reflected power. Not quite. SWR is an expression of the complex interaction (amplitude and phase) between waves of RF energy in a feed line. We measure SWR with SWR meters, typically installed at the transceiver (many transceivers have SWR metering built in).

The reason SWR is important is because it can play an enormous role in determining how much RF energy is lost in a feed line. The loss figures you see in Table 1.1 all assume that the SWR is 1:1. In other words, the feed line impedance is the same as the transceiver and antenna impedances and the RF energy flows from the transceiver to the antenna with little, if any, reflection. That's an idea situation, the *matched* condition, and it is one you'll rarely enjoy!

In real-world antenna systems, things are usually not perfect. As impedances in an antenna system become mismatched, SWR begins to rise. As the SWR increases, more RF energy is "tied up," so to speak, in the standing waves along the feed line. This wouldn't be a problem if you were using an exotic superconducting feed line with zero RF loss. All the RF would eventually be radiated by the antenna regardless of the SWR. (If you find a zero-loss feed line, there may be a Nobel Prize waiting for you.) But in our real-world feed line that RF energy will be lost as heat.

Assume 100 feet of RG58 coax with 100 W at 14 MHz applied by the transceiver (**Figure 1.39**). The characteristic impedance of the coax is 50 Ω and the antenna has been designed and adjusted to present a 50 Ω load. Congratulations, you have a matched condition and you can expect a total

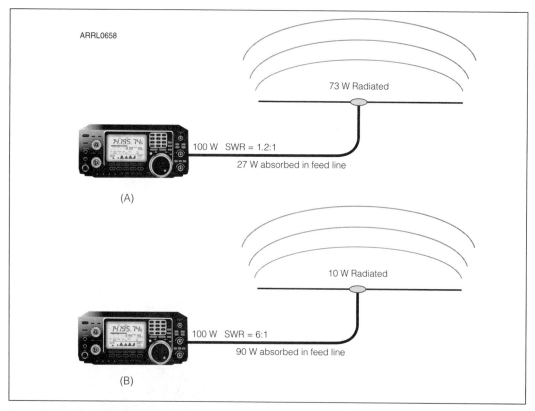

Figure 1.39 — A comparison of the effects of SWR. At (A) we have a 50 Ω feed line attached to the feed point of a dipole antenna, which is also approximately 50 Ω. The resulting SWR measured at the radio is about 1.2:1 and approximately 27 W is lost in the feed line. At (B) the SWR at the radio has jumped to 6:1 and now only 10 W is being radiated by the antenna. Of course, in the real world, the fold back circuit in the transceiver would never have permitted the radio to supply 100 W into a 6:1 SWR!

feed line loss of 1.33 dB, or about 27 W. Your SWR meter at the transceiver dutifully reports an SWR of about 1.2:1.

But now assume that a mischievous crow has landed on the antenna and tampered with the construction. As he flies away laughing, you notice that the SWR at your radio has suddenly jumped to 6:1. The impedance of the antenna at the feed point has strayed some distance from 50 Ω and now you have considerable amounts of 14 MHz RF energy in the form of standing waves between your radio and the antenna. That RG58 coax is dissipating your precious energy, resulting in a staggering loss of almost 10 dB. The 100 W produced by your radio has been reduced to a mere 10 W at your antenna. You are no longer smiling and your friends on the air are wondering what happened to your formerly strong signal.

Like all RF losses, the loss caused by SWR increases with frequency, the type of feed line, and the length of the feed line. Also, a high SWR condition can cause high voltage to exist at certain points, including at the output of your transceiver. This can easily damage modern solid-state radios. To protect your investment, many manufacturers have added so-called "SWR fold back" circuitry. When the SWR at the radio rises above about 1.5:1, the radio automatically begins to reduce (fold back) its output power.

You can negate the impact of SWR by adjusting the impedance at the antenna so that it more closely matches the feed line impedance. Many of the antennas and antenna designs in this book use this approach. Another technique is to disregard the mismatch at the antenna and instead transform the impedance mismatch to 50 Ω. This is when the *antenna tuner* comes into play.

An antenna tuner is really little more than a variable impedance transformer. It takes whatever impedance it finds on the feed line and matches it to 50 Ω for your transceiver. There are manual tuners that you adjust yourself, or automatic tuners that determine the correct settings at the press of a button, or at the moment you transmit. Combining an antenna tuner with low loss feed line seems like a sure cure for high SWR, but that isn't necessarily true.

Study **Figure 1.40**. The problem with an antenna tuner is that it only creates a 50 Ω impedance and a 1:1 SWR between its input and your transceiver. The SWR between the tuner output and the antenna *remains unchanged*. If you had a 6:1 SWR before you bought the antenna tuner, you'll have a 6:1 SWR after. The loss in the feed line is the same as it always was. The only difference is that now the transceiver fold back circuit will not reduce its output. Instead, it will deliver its full measure of power to the feed line. More power is indeed reaching the antenna, but an awful lot is also still being wasted, especially if the feed line is lossy.

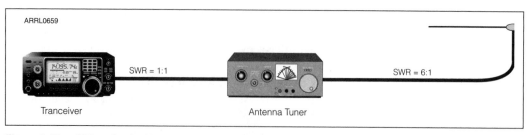

Figure 1.40 — Although an antenna tuner can provide a 50 Ω impedance and a 1:1 SWR to your transceiver, it does nothing whatsoever between the antenna tuner and the antenna. The SWR in that part of the antenna system remains unchanged.

This is not to say that antenna tuners are worthless. As I just mentioned, they make it possible to deliver more power to the feed line. And if you are using an extremely low-loss feed line such as ladder line, you can use an antenna tuner to match the ladder line impedance to your transceiver and take advantage of the fact that so little RF is lost even under extremely high SWR conditions. There are many hams who use ladder line and antenna tuners in exactly this fashion with excellent results. Sure, the SWR is high, but with the low loss of ladder line, it really doesn't matter.

There are also antenna tuners that are designed to be placed at or near the antenna itself. These remote antenna tuners adjust themselves automatically when they sense transmitted RF on the feed line, or when they receive a command from the transceiver. The great advantage of a remote tuner is that it creates a match between the feed point of the antenna (or at a point very close to it) and the feed line. This means that the resulting low SWR exists on the feed line all the way back to your transceiver, keeping loss to a bare minimum so that you can get away with using a feed line that is inexpensive and easy to install, such as coaxial cable. (See **Figure 1.41.**)

So let's condense our discussion of feed lines to four pertinent bullet points:

❑ The higher the frequency of the RF applied to a feed line, the greater the loss.

❑ The greater the length of a feed line, the greater the loss.

❑ The higher the SWR, the greater the loss.

❑ An antenna tuner does nothing to reduce feed line loss between the tuner and the antenna.

Ladder line is terrific for HF use if you can manage to get it back to your station without bending it at sharp angles or allowing it to come too close to lossy or metallic objects. Keep in mind, however, that you will *most definitely* need an antenna tuner at your radio to bridge the impedance gap

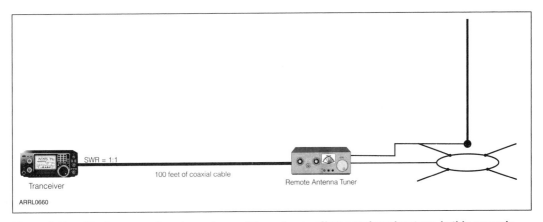

ARRL0660

Figure 1.41 — Placing a remote antenna tuner at the antenna offers a major advantage. In this example, the remote tuner is at the base of a vertical antenna. The tuner creates a 1:1 SWR (or something reasonably close to it) all the way back to the transceiver.

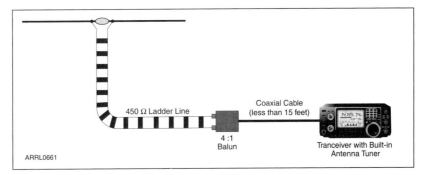

ARRL0661

Figure 1.42 — If you can't bring ladder line all the way back to your radio, here is an alternative. Use a 4:1 external balun to make the transition between the ladder line and a short (less than 15 foot) length of low loss coaxial cable. With luck, the antenna tuner at your station will be able to find an acceptable match on several bands this way. The reason for keeping the coax very short is because the SWR may be quite high at times. High SWR isn't a problem for ladder line, but it is for coax and the resulting loss may be substantial.

between the ladder line and the 50-Ω output of your transceiver. This can't be a tuner designed for coax; it must have a *balanced* input.

But what about transceivers with built-in antenna tuners? Most of these tuners are designed to handle limited impedance mismatches, like those typically resulting in a maximum SWR of 3:1. They are also designed for use with coaxial cable. These tuners were intended to "touch up" minor mismatches, such as when you choose to operate on a frequency that is a bit outside the SWR bandwidth of your antenna (for instance, when jumping from CW on 3.560 MHz where an antenna SWR might be 1.3:1 to SSB on 3.910 MHz where the SWR may rise to nearly 3:1).

On the other hand, it is possible to add a 4:1 balun (see **Figure 1.42**) to make the transition between the balanced ladder line and the unbalanced coaxial output. However, it is quite likely that the resulting impedance will still be outside the range of the transceiver tuner on some frequencies.

Chapter 2

Transceiver Choices

We could spend every page of this book talking about transceivers. There are so many possibilities to consider, it boggles the mind. Still, there are some common guidelines that apply.

Remember that the High Frequency or *HF* bands are defined as those groups of frequencies from 1.8 to 30 MHz. (Technically speaking, 1.8 MHz is in the Medium Frequency or MF region, but we won't argue definitions here!) These are the most popular Amateur Radio bands because they can be used to communicate throughout the world at any time of the day or night.

Hams use several different modes of communication on these bands:

❏ SSB — Single Sideband voice (the most popular voice mode)

❏ CW — Continuous Wave on/off keying using Morse code telegraphy

❏ Digital — Data communication using a variety of methods

❏ AM — Amplitude Modulated voice

❏ FM — Frequency Modulated voice (this takes place only on the high end of the HF spectrum from 29.5 to 29.7 MHz)

You'll find that most HF transceivers support all of these modes, although some radios lack FM and a few do not include AM. Most HF radios offer transmit coverage of all HF ham bands, plus the ability to listen to all frequencies throughout the HF range. This

The Icom IC-718 is an HF only transceiver that sells for less than $1000.

The Yaesu FT-450D transceiver includes the 6 meter band and sells for less than $1000.

The Alinco DX-SR8T is an HF-only transceiver that often retails for less than $700.

general-coverage receive capability is handy because it allows you to eavesdrop on short-wave broadcasts and other interesting signals.

HF transceivers typically offer 100 W output. With a decent antenna, this is enough power to make global contacts when the band is open. You'll also notice a few HF transceivers designed for low-power operating, better known as *QRP*. These transceivers are available in multimode, multiband models as well as single band, single mode units (usually CW only). QRP transceivers are often less expensive and physically smaller than their high-power cousins, but QRP hamming is an art unto itself and requires certain skills to be successful. See the sidebar "Is QRP Right for You?"

Is QRP Right for You?

Low power *QRP* operating is a thriving part of the Amateur Radio scene. QRP enthusiasts operate at only 5 watts output or less using primarily CW, but they also use digital modes and occasionally voice.

One great advantage of QRP is cost. A QRP transceiver built from a kit can cost less than $300. Low power consumption is an-

The Elecraft KX3 is among the most popular HF QRP transceivers on the market.

other major plus. QRP transceivers can be easily powered from batteries, which make them great for outdoor or emergency operating. A signal at QRP power levels is also much less likely to cause interference to you or your neighbors.

The disadvantage of QRP is that you need a very good antenna to make contacts with reasonable ease. With such low output power you must compensate at the antenna to make yourself heard. This isn't to say that you can't make QRP contacts with a poorer antenna (such as a small mobile antenna), but it will be much more difficult. You'll need to have considerable patience and perseverance since contacts may not come as easily to you as they would to someone running a 100 W transceiver.

HF Only or "DC to Daylight?"

The Kenwood TS-480SAT is a popular transceiver that can often be found selling for less than $1000.

The Elecraft K3 is an HF through 6 meter transceiver that comes in 10 W and 100 W versions, as well as kit or factory assembled models. Prices vary with the most expensive model being the factory assembled 100 W K3 selling for about $2400.

The transceiver trend in recent years has been away from HF-only radios. In the 1990s Icom introduced the IC-706, the first multimode transceiver that spanned the HF bands *and* the 6- and 2-meter VHF bands. Other manufacturers followed suit and now you'll find transceivers that cover 1.8 to 54 MHz and even 1.8 to 450 MHz in a single box. These so-called "dc to daylight" transceivers are among the most popular radios sold today. It's easy to see why. They offer the ability to enjoy the global coverage of the HF bands while opening the door to the enjoyment of VHF and UHF.

Many of these dc-to-daylight transceivers are also quite compact, serving as either mobile or base radios. Others offer extended features such as the ability to function as amateur satellite transceivers.

Software Defined Radios

Software Defined Radios (SDRs) are in a class by themselves. Unlike traditional HF transceivers that take received signals from the antenna, amplify, filter, and then demodulate to audio for your speaker or headphones, SDRs convert the signal at or near the antenna directly to digital information. Once the signal is rendered to data, the software in your computer can massage that data and demodulate almost any type of signal imaginable. The software can also create ultra-sharp filters that are adjustable to any width you require.

When it is time to transmit, the SDR software performs the same magic in reverse. It takes the analog audio signal from your microphone (if you're in the SSB mode), converts it to data, processes the data as needed to create the necessary signal, and then converts back to analog for amplification. The result is an RF signal that is applied to your antenna.

The first SDRs were introduced to the ham community in the early

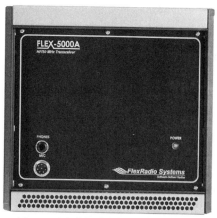

A software defined radio such as this FlexRadio Flex-5000A isn't much to look at because the real action is taking place on your computer monitor.

2000s. At the time this book was written, SDR transceivers had become commonplace with about 20% of all Amateur Radio HF stations having an SDR in residence. This trend is expected to continue.

The SDR advantage is its extreme flexibility. The way the radio operates is almost entirely dependent on the software — change the software and you've essentially changed the radio. In a crude sense, the hardware part of the radio functions as a sophisticated analog-to-digital (and vice versa) conversion device. When you're receiving, the analog RF signals go to into the SDR's antenna jack and data comes out the other end. It is up to the software running on your computer to take that data and extract the signal you wish to hear (or create the signal you wish to transmit). A well-designed Software Defined Radio can offer performance that is substantially superior to a traditional HF transceiver of the same price class.

This flexibility makes it possible for an SDR to evolve over time. A software defined radio can be instantly upgraded with new features and improvements simply by loading new software. Compare that to a traditional hardware transceiver that is difficult (sometimes impossible) to upgrade

The Flex-5000A in operation.

without modifying circuits and swapping out various components.

The disadvantage of an SDR is the fact that it requires a computer to function. Without a computer to process data from the SDR, the radio is useless. This can be a problem if you want to take your SDR on the road, since you'll always have to pack a laptop computer with the rest of your gear. In addition, the present generation of SDRs requires a certain amount of computer expertise on the part of the operator. You'll be expected to install and configure software, with some of the applications being a bit complex.

Which Transceiver is Right for You?

The answer to this question depends on how much money you have to spend and what you hope to do with the radio once you buy it. You can spend as little as $200 and as much as $17,000!

For casual chit-chat operating, just about any HF transceiver will do the job. It's when you begin hunting for weak signals, or operating in contests, that receiver performance becomes particularly important.

The ancient axiom "you get what you pay for" is as true in Amateur Radio as it is anywhere else. You can save a bundle of money with a low-end transceiver, but don't expect high-end receiver performance. If you expect to be a competitive contester or DXer, it pays to invest in a higher-end traditional transceiver or SDR that will give you the ability to hold your own in challenging environments. This means powerful filtering options and enhanced IMD performance to keep nearby interference at bay.

The best approach to sorting out your transceiver options is to become a member of the ARRL. You'll receive *QST* magazine each month with its detailed Product Reviews and have access to the ARRL online Product Review archives. By carefully studying the *QST* reviews you can make an informed choice, getting maximum "bang" for your buck. Even if you don't fully understand the Product Review test results, look for the key results table. This colorful graphic will tell you how the radio performed in all the areas that matter most.

Bells and Whistles

Every transceiver has a collection of features, and some are more important than others. The number of features directly affects the price you'll pay. More features = more money. In ham slang, features are known as "bells and whistles."

Let's talk about several common features of traditional HF transceiver (not SDRs) and rate their overall *operating enjoyment factor…*

❏ Noise Blanker

Operating Enjoyment Factor: *High*

Noise blankers are your best friends when you're doing battle with local noise sources, especially rhythmic noises such as the sharp *putt-putt-putts* of engine spark plugs. A well-designed noise blanker can make this annoying noise disappear. Good noise blankers are critical for HF mobile operating.

❏ Audio DSP

Operating Enjoyment Factor: *Medium*

Audio DSP means digital signal processing at the audio output stage of the transceiver. Audio DSP can significantly reduce noise, and many DSP designs can also eliminate the squeal you'll hear on the HF bands when an interfering station transmits a continuous unmodulated signal on the frequency you are receiving. However, some amateurs complain that DSP noise reduction imparts a "hollow," distorted character to the signal that they find annoying.

❏ IF DSP

Operating Enjoyment Factor: *High*

Digital signal processing at the receiver's intermediate frequency (IF) is something you'll find in moderately priced (or higher) transceivers. Don't confuse this with audio-stage DSP.

Lower-cost transceivers use mechanical or crystal filters in the IF stage to reduce the receiver bandwidth and eliminate interference in a fixed range of frequencies. These filters tend to be expensive (as much as $200 each) and you have to purchase them at an additional cost. In contrast, DSP IF filters are provided as standard equipment; you don't need to buy them later. Better yet, they can be adjusted to achieve whatever bandwidth you desire. Many high performance radios combine IF DSP and hardware filters.

❏ Speech Processing

Operator Enjoyment Factor: *Low*

Speech processing, sometimes called "speech compression," is a method of boosting the average output power in an SSB voice signal. It can make a difference if you are using low power and you're trying to make yourself heard through interference or poor band conditions. However, speech processing can also introduce distortion if not used properly. This is a nice-to-have feature if you are into SSB, but not strictly necessary.

❑ IF Shift

Operating Enjoyment Factor: *Medium*

The IF Shift function allows you to change the receiver's intermediate frequency slightly to "move" it off an interfering signal. If you're into CW, IF Shift can be quite useful in crowded conditions, but its benefits on SSB are less pronounced.

❑ Built-in SWR Meter

Operating Enjoyment Factor: *High*

As you may remember from Chapter 1, knowing your antenna system SWR is critical. SWR—Standing Wave Ratio—is an indicator of how well your antenna system is matched to your radio. A poor match, which shows up as a high SWR, will cause your transceiver to reduce its output and may even result in damage to your equipment. Many hams purchase outboard SWR meters as separate station accessories, but if your radio already includes the meter, so much the better.

❑ Built-in Automatic Antenna Tuner

Operating Enjoyment Factor: *Medium*

Depending on the type of antenna system you use, this feature can be either extremely useful or totally useless. Built-in tuners work well when you need to match your radio to an antenna system with a reasonably low SWR (less than 3:1). For antenna systems with high SWRs, they offer little benefit. Some transceivers, such as some Elecraft models, offer wide-range antenna tuners, but this is not common.

❑ Computer Interface

Operating Enjoyment Factor: *High*

Computers and transceivers go hand-in-hand these days. If you want to be able to tie your radio and computer together (for memory programming, automatic frequency logging, etc), look for this feature. *Beware:* Some transceivers include the complete interface while others make it available only as an option at an additional price.

❑ Voice Operated Switch (VOX)

Operating Enjoyment Factor: *Low*

If you are a voice operator, VOX can be useful because it frees you from having to repeatedly press the **TRANSMIT/RECEIVE** switch. Whenever you stop talking, VOX will switch your transceiver back to receive automatically. When you speak again, VOX will place your radio in the transmit mode.

The downside of VOX is that it can be annoying—both to you and the listener. It will do its duty every time you pause to consider a thought, popping the radio rapidly from transmit to receive and back again. This causes the "ahh" effect—the tendency for VOX users to say "ahhhhhh" to keep their radios transmitting while they think of what they want to say next!

❏ CW Keyer

Operating Enjoyment Factor: *High*

If you are into CW operating, this is an important feature. Many CW operators use "paddles" that work with CW keyers to automatically generate dots and dashes whenever you touch them. You can buy external CW keyers, but having the keyer already built into the radio is highly desirable.

If you're leaning toward a software-defined transceiver, the bells and whistles reside mostly in the software, although there are still several feature-centric factors to keep in mind.

❏ Many SDR transceivers do not include SWR metering. Plan on having to purchase an SWR/power meter separately.

❏ Not all SDRs offer 100 W output; some feature as little as 1 W output. Evaluate the specifications carefully.

❏ CW operation can be problematic with some types of SDR transceivers, and many do not include CW keyers. If CW is important to you, check this specification and, most important, check either the *QST* review of the transceiver, or comments from online sources such as reviews on eHam (**www.eham.net**).

What About Used Transceivers?

So far we've talked about buying new radios, but there are a large number of hams that prefer used equipment. Buying used will save you money in most cases. Of course, the older the radio, the less compatible it will be with modern technology. Older radios also have a tendency to break down (they have suffered years of wear and tear, after all). When this happens, replacement parts and repair services may be difficult to find.

As a rule of thumb, stick with used transceivers that are fewer than 15 years old if you lack the technical skills to do your own repairs. See the sidebar, "Shopping for Equipment." Also be aware of the fact

This Kenwood TS-520 transceiver was sold in the 1970s. Notice the vacuum tube driver and amplifier section in the lower right corner. If you purchase a used transceiver from this era, you may need to replace increasingly hard-to-find tubes.

The Yaesu FT-100D is similar to the Icom IC-706 and was also manufactured in the early 2000s. Like the '706, you'll find it on the used market for less than $500.

This Icom IC-706MkIIG 100-W transceiver was sold in the early 2000s. It offers HF through 70 cm in a compact package. You'll often find used models for less than $500.

If you're looking for something larger in a used HF transceiver, this Kenwood TS-570 was manufactured in the early 2000s and sells for less than $700 on the used equipment market today.

Shopping for Equipment

If you are looking for new ham equipment, one of your best resources is *QST* magazine, the journal of the American Radio Relay League (ARRL). The magazine is mailed to you each month as part of your ARRL membership (call 860-594-0200, or see the League on the Web at **www.arrl.org**). *QST* meticulously reviews new Amateur Radio equipment in each issue. The magazine also carries advertisements from ham dealers and manufacturers so you can keep up to date with all the new products on the market.

If you have a ham dealer near you, that's a great place to shop. At the dealer's store you can get your hands on the radio and ask questions about it. If you can't get to the store, however, most dealers have Web sites and toll-free telephone numbers. Just look at their advertisements in *QST*.

If you prefer used equipment, you'll find that most of these sales occur online. eBay (**www.ebay.com**) has tons of ham gear for auction every day.

Dealers often sell used equipment in their stores and on their Web sites. The dealer advantage is that they offer limited used-equipment warranties. This takes much of the worry out of your used-equipment purchase.

It probably goes without saying that you need to be careful when purchasing used equipment. See the equipment and operate it "in person" whenever possible. When shopping eBay auctions, look for sellers that have very good "feedback" ratings, ideally 100% positive. Make sure you read the auction description very carefully. If you have questions, e-mail the seller before you bid.

that radios made prior to the late 1970s will likely contain vacuum tubes. While tubes are still available in the ham community, they are becoming scarce and expensive as time goes on.

Roll Your Own?

Most hams buy their radios factory assembled, but it is possible to *build* your radio as well. QRP enthusiasts, in particular, are fond of building their own transceivers from kits, or even just from diagrams published in books and magazines. Most of QRP transceivers are single-band, CW-only rigs, but there are exceptions.

Kit building is fun and educational, and you'll save a considerable amount of money in the process. If you think your technical skills are marginal, however, build your kit with the help of a more knowledgeable ham.

You can build a tiny QRP transceiver from a kit.

Power Supplies

Without a power supply, a transceiver is a lifeless hunk of metal and plastic. The power supply provides the "juice" that makes ham radio possible. Only high-end transceivers include their own power supplies, so unless you have one of these radios on your list, plan on having to purchase a power supply for your station.

A typical 100 W transceiver requires a power supply that can deliver about 25 A of current at 13.8 V when you are operating the radio at "full throttle." That kind of power supply will set you back about $100 to $200, depending on the design. QRP transceivers, on the other hand, have far lower power requirements. A much less expensive 3 A 13.8 V supply should be more than sufficient.

Don't worry about buying a power supply with too much current capacity. Your equipment will draw only the current it needs— no more, no less. In fact, it is probably safe to say that you can never have too much current capacity. It may seem economically foolish to invest $200 in

A switching power supply like this one offers high current capacity in a small, lightweight package.

Linear power supplies tend to be large and heavy, but they have a well-earned reputation for ruggedness.

a 25-A power supply when all you want to power is a 5-W QRP rig. However, if you think you'll be upgrading to a larger radio in the near future, you may want to get the big power supply today (especially if you find a great deal on a high-current supply).

When shopping for a power supply, beware of one potential stumbling block. Power supplies are often rated by their *continuous* and *intermittent* (ICS) current capacities. The figure you want to look at is the *continuous* rating—the amount of current the power supply can provide continuously. Don't be misled by an advertisement that promises a fantastic deal on, say, a 30-A supply. Are those 30 amps provided intermittently—only for short periods of time—or continuously? You need continuous power, so check and be sure!

It is also worth mentioning that you'll find two types of ham-grade power supplies for sale. The *linear* design uses a hefty transformer to shift the 120 V ac line voltage from your wall outlet to a lower voltage for later conversion to 13.8 V dc. These power supplies tend to be large and heavy, especially the high-current models.

Another approach to the power supply problem is the *switching* design. In the switching power supply, the ac line voltage is converted directly to dc and filtered. This high-voltage dc is then fed to a power oscillator that "switches" it on and off at a rate of about 20 to 500 kHz. The result is pulsating dc that can be applied to a transformer for conversation to 13.8 V or whatever is needed. The reason for doing this is that rapidly pulsating dc can be transformed to lower voltages without the need for large transformers. It is the transformer that accounts for most of the weight, size, and cost of traditional linear power supplies. A switching power supply is much smaller and lighter, and usually less expensive.

Switching power supplies are the same type found in your computer and they are becoming more popular in Amateur Radio. The disadvantage of the switching supply is that some designs generate interfering signals that you can hear in your radio. If you're considering a switching power supply, look for models that boast low "RFI" (radio frequency interference). *QST* magazine occasionally reviews and tests switching power supplies. If you are an ARRL member, you can read previously published *QST* reviews on the ARRLWeb (**www.arrl.org**).

Chapter 3

Do You Need an Amplifier?

If we're talking about first HF stations, is it appropriate to even bring up the subject of amplifiers? After all, don't most amateurs add amplifiers later, when they've already established their primary stations?

For the most part, yes. Amplifiers are often purchased after the fact, after the station operator has had time to see if an amplifier is really necessary. But the realization that an amplifier is definitely in your future may come much sooner than you think, so let's spend a couple of pages discussing the pros and cons so you'll be prepared when the time comes.

The Effects of Increasing Power

Most HF transceivers offer 100 W output. If you feed 100 W to a good antenna system, especially a directional antenna, 100 W is *usually*

The Ameritron ALS-1300 is an economical solid-state amplifier.

The ACOM 1500 is a full legal-limit power amplifier.

adequate to work almost any location in the world under normal conditions.

But there will be times when 100 W, even to an optimal antenna, simply won't cut it. This will happen when propagation conditions are poor, when interference is intense, or some combination of both. Under those conditions extra power can make the difference between making contact and giving up.

Hams often equate results of increasing power with elevated readings on a transceiver's *S meter*. S meters — signal strength meters — are standard equipment on most transceivers. We use them as yardsticks to compare the strengths of received signals. During voice conversations (AM or SSB), you'll hear hams refer to the strengths of signals according to readings on their S meters.

"You are a solid S9 this afternoon, Tom."

An S meter reading of 9 is quite good; it means the signal is very strong. But if Tom's signal drops to S3, does that mean his signal is necessarily "bad?" If Tom can still be heard and understood clearly, the answer is "no." What matters is the *quality* of the communication — how well the signal is understood at the receiving end. This is true for any mode, including CW or digital. With that in mind, it's obvious that an S meter reading has little to do with communication quality or effectiveness. An S meter measures signal strength *only*.

Adding an amplifier to your station will boost the strength of your signal, meaning that it will result in a higher S meter indication on the receiving end. However, it will not necessarily boost the quality of your signal. Signal quality is about more than brute strength, it also involves factors such as noise and other interference at the receiving station. Increasing signal strength will help overcome the other factors that might reduce quality, but don't rely on it to solve reception problems completely.

And What About Those S Meters?

A veteran ham once told me that he wished S meters had never been invented. "They do more harm than good. Many hams have come to believe that S meters are the ultimate judges of signals. If their signal doesn't kick their buddy's meter up to a certain level, it's time to pour money into an amplifier. The only goal is to get the meter at their buddy's station to bounce higher and higher. What a waste!"

The old timer was a little harsh in his judgment of S meters, but there is some truth in what he was saying. Most transceiver S meters offer approximate measurements at best. In an ideal meter, for example, an increase of one S unit is supposed to be the equivalent of a 6 dB increase in signal strength. Tests have shown, however, that S meter accuracy can vary significantly from one radio to another.

But let's assume that you have a friend in a distant city who owns a transceiver with a precision S meter, one that is finely calibrated to measure each 6 dB increase in signal strength as exactly one S unit. Let's also assume that you are running 100 W of power on 20 meters and your friend is reporting that your signal is registering a mere S1 on his meter (**Figure 3.1**).

On your station desk you have a 1500 W amplifier that is presently set for just 500 W output. Reach over and switch it on. Now your station output jumps to 500 W.

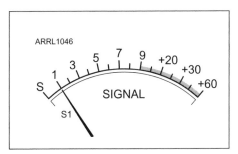

Figure 3.1 — With 100 W output, your signal is a mere S 1 on your friend's S meter.

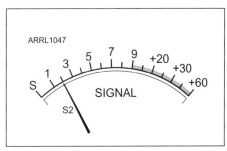

Figure 3.2 — Increasing power to 500 W bounces your signal up to S 2.

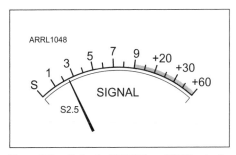

Figure 3.3 — Going to 1000 W from 100 W output results in your signal reaching S 2.5 at your friend's station.

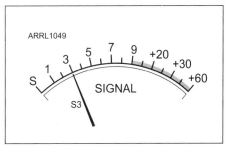

Figure 3.4 — Running the amplifier all the way up to 1500 W output only moves your original S 1 signal to S 3.

Your friend reports that your signal has only increased to a little more than S2 (**Figure 3.2**). That won't do! Increase the output to 1000 W.

Now your friend reports that your signal has pushed its way up to just 2½ S units (**Figure 3.3**). Wouldn't you expect more from 1000 W? Better run the throttle all the way to 1500 W — the full legal limit on 20 meters.

Your friend now reports the result — a whopping S3 (**Figure 3.4**). How can this be? Shouldn't you be practically pinning his meter to the wall with 1500 W?

Sorry, but you've just discovered an important truth: increasing power can improve signal quality, but it may not make a huge difference in signal strength as measured on an S meter. Going from 100 W to 1500 W is an increase of 12 dB, which translates to a jump from S1 to S3 — *just two S units*. You've spent a large sum of money just to move someone's S meter two places. Now you also know why shortwave broadcasters use tens of thousands of watts of output power. It takes that kind of RF muscle to make a big difference to a receiver on the other side of the world. As a ham you don't have nearly that kind of power available.

This does not mean that buying an amplifier is a waste of money. As we discussed earlier, a large power boost can definitely make the difference when the going gets rough. If you expect to be a competitive DXer or contester, an RF amplifier is a worthwhile investment.

In other words, if you purchase an amplifier, do it for the right reasons. Buy an amplifier to give your signal an edge under difficult conditions, *not* because you think you need to measure up to an arbitrary reading on another ham's S meter (his meter may not be properly calibrated anyway). If your signal is strong enough to be clearly understood at its destination, that's all that matters.

Amplifier Pros and Cons

❏ **Pro:** As we've already stated, an amplifier can give your signal a much needed edge when conditions become challenging.

❏ **Pro:** Amplifiers are easy to install and operate. A couple of cable connections is all it takes. More expensive amplifiers even offer automatic band switching — when you change bands at your transceiver, the amplifier changes bands as well.

❏ **Pro:** Amplifiers are reliable. Despite all the RF power they produce, modern amplifier designs are highly reliable. Even solid state power amps, which used to have a reputation for being "fragile," are now every bit as rugged as venerable tube-based models.

❏ **Con:** You may need to modify your electrical wiring to accommodate

The SPE 2K-FA solid state amplifier switches bands automatically.

the needs of the amplifier. Many amplifiers require 240 Vac. If you don't have a 240 Vac outlet in your station, you will need to add one. The cost of hiring an electrician to install the line and outlet is an expense you'll need to take into account.

❑ **Con:** If you are already causing interference to the electronics in your home or your neighbor's home, increasing power with an amplifier will make the situation worse — guaranteed.

❑ **Con:** You may need to upgrade other aspects of your station to accommodate the higher power levels. Any antenna tuners, coaxial switches and other devices must be rated for the expected power levels.

Chapter 4

Computers and Software

Your first HF station does not need a computer. In fact, you can expect endless hours of enjoyment from your station without a computer anywhere in sight.

But...

Most Amateur Radio stations include a computer, and they do so for three reasons:

❑ Logging
❑ Contesting
❑ Digital operating

You can certainly keep your station log on paper, but maintaining a log in software greatly enhances your ability to keep track of contacts and, most important, monitor your progress toward various operating awards. And with a large portion of the ham community applying for awards electronically by way of ARRL's online Logbook of The World system (**www.arrl. org/logbook-of-the-world**), you probably don't want to be left out.

In the world of contesting, software is almost mandatory. Computers and software have become essential tools for keeping track of progress in contests — how many multipliers you've worked, your *rate* (number of contacts per hour), your current score and much more — and helping you avoid the dreaded *dupe* (working a station more than once on a given band). Contesting software may also send and receive CW, RTTY, or other modes and offer so-called *voice keying* — sending pre-recorded voice tracks such as a CQ call. With so many contests requiring that logs be submitted in electronic formats, contest software is needed for that function as well.

Finally, having a computer at your station opens the door to digital operating in dozens of modes. Many amateurs are chasing DX using digital modes such as RTTY (radio teletype), PSK31, and JT65. In fact, if you are forced to operate at low power with indoor antennas, being able to get on the air with digital modes will make a huge difference in your ability to enjoy Amateur Radio.

You can also use your computer for more "exotic" activities such as bouncing digital signals off the trails of meteors as they plunge into the atmosphere, exchanging digital images over the airwaves, or trying your hand at low power propagation studies.

Radios for Digital Modes

Modern radios get along surprisingly well with computers. In fact, most modern HF transceivers are designed with computers in mind. They offer a variety of computer-friendly connections in the form of "ports," depending on the model in question.

Nearly every HF rig manufactured within the past decade includes an "accessory" port of some kind. Typically this is a multipin jack (as many as 13 pins) that provides connections for audio into and out of the radio, as well as a pin that causes the radio to switch from receive to transmit whenever the pin is grounded. This is often called the *PTT* or *Push To Talk* line. Some manufacturers also call it the "Send" line. Take a look at the typical accessory jack shown in **Figure 4.1**.

These accessory ports are ideal for connecting the kinds of interface devices we use to operate HF digital, as well as pass information automatically to logging and contest software. In addition to the PTT function, accessory ports often provide receive audio output at *fixed* levels that never change no matter where the VOLUME knob is set. This is a highly convenient feature that you'll appreciate when operating late at night after everyone has gone to bed. You can turn the VOLUME knob to zero and still have all the receive audio you need!

Be aware that some radio manufacturers label accessory ports as "data" or "digital" ports. This causes no end of confusion because modern rigs often offer two types of connections: a true accessory port with audio and transmit/receive keying lines and another port that allows a computer to "talk" to the radio. The confusion occurs when hams attempt to figure out which ports they need to use.

For the purpose of getting on the air with many

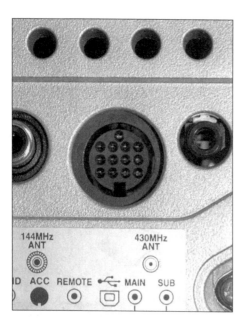

Figure 4.1 — A typical transceiver accessory port. This one happens to offer 13 pins.

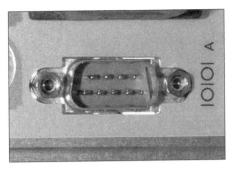

A typical RS232 serial port.

HF digital modes, the only type of radio "control" we care about is the ability to switch from receive to transmit and back again. That connection is available at the accessory port, even though the port may go by a different name.

The kind of control the transceiver manufacturers have in mind goes way beyond the act of simply switching between transmit and receive. They are talking about the computer taking over almost every function of the radio; that's a different animal entirely. Full computer control usually involves software that does many things, such as displaying and changing the transceiver's frequency, raising and lowering the audio level, scanning memory frequencies, and a great deal more. Some computer control software is so elaborate that the radio itself can be placed out of sight and all control conducted at the keyboard and monitor screen. Many amateurs use this capability to control their rigs remotely over the Internet at great distances. Other programs, such as logging software, have the ability to automatically log the transceiver frequency.

Transceivers have separate ports for this type of computer interfacing and these most definitely are *not* accessory ports. On the contrary, they are ports strictly designed to swap data with external computers. They come in several varieties …

TTL: Transistor-Transistor Logic. These ports require a special interface to translate the serial communication from your computer to TTL pulses that your radio can comprehend.

USB: Universal Serial Bus. Although the consumer electronics world adopted USB years ago, transceiver manufacturers have been somewhat slower to catch on.

RS232: This is a serial port that can be connected directly to your computer if your computer has a serial (COM) port. Most modern computers have done away with serial ports, but you can use a USB-to-serial converter to bridge the gap.

Ethernet: This port allows the transceiver to become a "network device," just like your wireless router, printer, etc. Only a handful of transceivers offer Ethernet ports at this time.

To get on the air and enjoy HF digital, you do not need full computer control and you do not need to concern yourself with this transceiver port. The accessory jack (or whatever your radio manufacturer calls it) is the only port that matters.

An adaptor that allows a serial port to communicate with a USB port.

Duty Cycle

When talking about using your transceiver and computer to operate digital modes, we need to spend a little time discussing the concept of *duty cycle*. A somewhat crude definition of duty cycle is the time that a radio spends generating RF output as a fraction of the total time under consideration. In HF digital terms, think of duty cycle as the amount of time your radio is generating RF during any given transmission compared to the amount of the time during the same transmission when RF output falls to zero. A 100% duty cycle would mean that your radio is cranking out RF continuously throughout the entire transmission; the RF output level never falls to zero.

Now you may say, "I guess I'm always using a 100% duty cycle. After all, my radio is always generating RF whenever I'm transmitting."

Not necessarily.

When you are transmitting digital, CW, or even SSB voice, your rig may not be operating at a 100% duty cycle. Consider SSB voice as an example. Whenever you speak into the microphone, the RF output level changes dramatically as your voice changes. It can go from 100% output to zero in a fraction of a second. The same is true for CW. Whenever your CW key is open between the dots and dashes, your transceiver output is at zero.

Measured over a period of time (your transmitting time), the duty cycle of SSB voice is actually about 40%; CW is often as low as 30% or even less if you are a particularly slow sender. HF digital modes also vary in duty cycle. Some modes such as radioteletype (RTTY) push your radio to a duty cycle of nearly 100%. Others result in much lower duty cycles.

So why should you care about your duty cycle?

The answer is that your radio may not be designed for the type of punishment a high duty cycle transmission can inflict. When you operate your radio at a 100% duty cycle, which can occur often if you are operating digital modes, you are demanding that its final amplifier circuits produce the full measure of output — whatever you've set that output level to be — for the entire time you are transmitting. The result is heat, and potentially a lot of it. Apply enough heat to a circuit for a sufficient length of time and you'll see components begin to fail, sometimes in spectacular fashion.

Some manufacturers don't consider the possibility that their SSB voice transceivers might be pressed into service as digital transceivers. They design the radios to tolerate the duty cycle of a typical voice transmission. If you use this same radio to enjoy a high duty cycle digital mode such as RTTY, you could be asking the radio to operate well outside its design limits — with unfortunate results.

Always read your transceiver manual before attempting to use the radio for digital operating. The manufacturer may advise you to reduce the RF output by as much as 50% when using high duty cycle modes. This keeps the heat generation manageable. When in doubt, or when you notice that your radio is becoming particularly hot, reduce the RF output. You'll find that digital modes don't require a great deal of output power anyway, so chances are you won't notice the 50% reduction.

Transceiver Filters

When it comes to digital operating, another important transceiver feature to consider is receive filtering. In most cases we're talking about the filters located in the Intermediate Frequency (IF) stage of your radio. These can be physical filters: modules that plug in or are soldered into the radio's circuit board. Many modern transceivers use Digital Signal Processing (DSP) at the IF stage rather than physical filters. The advantage of DSP is that it is often designed to be continuously variable. This means that you can narrow or expand the filter with the push of a button or the twist of a knob.

Most popular HF digital modes use wide receive-audio bandwidths for reception, so it isn't strictly necessary to have an IF filter narrower than the typical SSB voice bandwidth of about 2.8 kHz. All SSB transceivers meet this requirement.

There are some important exceptions, though. If you decide to try your hand at RTTY contest operating, you'll quickly discover that a 2.8 kHz IF bandwidth is entirely too wide. You won't be able to easily separate individual signals in a sea of RTTY contest chaos. In this environment you need to narrow the IF bandwidth to at least 500 Hz. In ultra-crowded conditions you may need a bandwidth as narrow as 300 Hz.

There may be other situations where you'll want to use a narrower IF bandwidth. Let's say you are trying to communicate with a weak station and a much stronger station begins transmitting a rock-crushing signal about 1 kHz up the band. Your radio's Automatic Gain Control (AGC) is going to respond by dropping your receiver sensitivity into the basement. The weak station will become weaker still, or disappear altogether.

It isn't practical to ask the gigawatt station to move, so your only alternative is to dramatically narrow your IF bandwidth to the point where his signal is eliminated and only the weak signal remains. Continuously adjustable IF DSP filtering is terrific for this application. You can create an IF filter as narrow as necessary and put it right on the signal you are trying to hear. With ultra-sharp DSP filters, everything outside the passband is effectively gone.

If your transceiver already has selectable or variable IF filters, you're all set. If not, consider adding a 500 Hz IF filter if your radio will allow you to do so. It could cost you as much as $150, but it is a good investment in the future, especially for contesting.

AFSK vs FSK

Here is an interesting point that often causes consternation among digital operators when they consider their HF transceiver options.

Basic HF SSB transceivers typically offer at least three operating modes: Upper Sideband (USB), Lower Sideband (LSB), and CW. Others include AM and even FM. For HF digital operation USB or LSB is all you need.

That said, you'll also notice that some HF rigs include a digital mode selection that may be labeled "RTTY," "Digital," or "Data." Here is where the gnashing of teeth begins because the way the radio behaves when you select this mode can vary depending on the design. In other words, these labels can mean different things in different radios.

For instance, the "Digital" mode may simply control how the IF filters can be used. The radio may forbid you from selecting a narrow IF filter when you are in one of the SSB modes, but it will suddenly relent and allow you to access a narrow filter when you enter the "Data" mode. It may also include a function that "looks" for the incoming audio at the accessory jack whenever you select the "Data" mode. Otherwise it ignores the incoming audio at the accessory jack entirely. This is odd design behavior, but it happens.

What is most important for our discussion, however, is the fact that some manufacturers use this mode label to indicate that the radio will switch to *FSK*. What does this mean?

The vast majority of HF digital operators use Audio Frequency Shift Keying or *AFSK*, although they may not realize it. The audio tones from their sound devices are applied to their radios and converted to shifting RF frequencies at the output, hence the term *Audio* Frequency Shift Keying.

But there is yet another way to create shifting RF. You can take data pulses directly from the computer (not sound) and use those pulses to directly shift a transceiver's master oscillator from one RF frequency to another. Since there is no audio involved, this is known as Frequency Shift Keying or *FSK*.

Is there an advantage to using FSK vs AFSK? Not really. It is mostly a matter of convenience. Some HF digital transceivers will not allow you to use narrow IF filters unless you operate using the FSK mode (this design quirk is in decline, though).

The problem with FSK in amateur transceivers is that it is limited to shifting between only two frequencies. Many amateur digital modes use more than two frequencies. PSK31 — the most popular digital mode — doesn't shift frequency at all; it shifts *phase* instead. The only common digital mode that can benefit from true FSK is RTTY since RTTY signals shift between only two frequencies.

FSK as it exists in Amateur Radio transceivers is a feature for RTTY aficionados alone. The irony is that it is impossible to tell the difference between a properly modulated AFSK RTTY signal and a RTTY signal generated by FSK.

So why bother? Again, the answer is convenience — the FSK RTTY operator never has to worry about sending too much audio to his radio, and at the same time he is assured of having full access to all the IF filters that might otherwise be missing if he wasn't using this mode.

If your transceiver offers a "RTTY," "Data," or "Digital" mode, read your manual carefully and find out exactly what this means. Chances are that "RTTY" means FSK. "Data" or "Digital" likely means AFSK, although even the manufacturers confuse the terminology. You'll find some manuals referring to AFSK as FSK. The authors are not wrong, strictly speaking. After all, regardless of whether you're using AFSK or FSK the RF signal frequencies at the output are still shifting back and forth. It is "frequency shift keying" in either case. The difference is in the method you use to create the shifty signals.

If you're unsure, look at the hookup diagram in the manual. Does it show digital transmit audio being applied to the radio at the accessory or microphone jack? If so, it is AFSK. When you select the "Digital" or "Data" mode, you're really in the SSB mode, but using audio to generate the frequency changes.

But if the manual shows keying data being supplied to an "FSK" line, it is indeed true FSK.

Computer Choices

From the early 1980s through about 2005, the desktop computer was king among ordinary consumers and Amateur Radio operators. This is a computer in a separate, stand-alone case connected to a monitor screen, keyboard, and mouse. Inside the computer case there is a sound device of some sort, either a dedicated *sound card* or a set of sound-processing chips on the motherboard. The computer connects to peripheral devices through the use of serial (COM) ports.

From 2005 onward we saw two important changes. One was the fact that laptop computers because more powerful and affordable. The other was that serial ports disappeared in favor of USB ports in both laptops *and* desktop machines.

By 2010 laptops began to dominate Amateur Radio stations. As hams upgraded their computers, they no longer saw the need for bulky desktop systems when sleek laptops would do quite nicely.

As this book went to press, even laptops were facing stiff competition from *tablet* computers such as the Apple iPad. In Amateur Radio stations, laptops and desktops are still the most popular computers, but this is likely to change as more ham applications are developed for tablets.

For now, however, our focus will remain primarily on laptops and desktops. With that in mind, what kind of laptop or desktop do you need for your station?

The good news is that most Amateur Radio software does not require powerful computers. Any ordinary off-the-shelf consumer-grade computer—desktop or laptop—will do the job. If you are buying new, don't overspend for a powerful computer you won't need. Frankly, a decent used computer that's only a couple of years old will be more than adequate.

In terms of operating systems, the vast majority of Amateur Radio software is written for Microsoft *Windows*. Some of these programs were created during the *Windows XP* era, but they run well on both *Windows Vista* and *Windows 7* and *Windows 8*. Some amateurs have reported problems with older software running under 64-bit *Windows 7* and *8*, but in my experience this problem is uncommon.

There is ham software available for *MacOS* as well, although not as much variety. *Linux* users will find a number of ham applications, too.

If you are considering a new or used computer (desktop or laptop), here are a few rule-of-thumb shopping specifications:

The desktop computer for your station doesn't need to be overly powerful.

This economical laptop would be perfectly adequate as a station computer.

❑ The processor clock frequency ("speed") should be 1.5 GHz or better.

❑ The computer should have as much memory as possible, not just to run the ham applications smoothly, but the operating system as well. For *Windows 7* or *8*, I'd recommend at least 4 GB of RAM; more is always better.

❑ Either a built-in wireless (Wi-Fi) modem or an Ethernet port. Although it isn't necessary for ham work, chances are you'll want to connect your station to the Internet from time to time. If so, you'll need a wireless modem or Ethernet port to do so.

❑ A CD-ROM drive for loading new software that is available only on CD (a less common need today, but don't sell yourself short).

The Importance of Computer Sound

With few exceptions, every computer you are likely to purchase today will include a either a dedicated sound card or a sound chipset. This feature is absolutely critical for HF digital operation because most of the modes you'll enjoy depend on sound devices to act as radio *modems — mod*ulators/ *dem*odulators.

The audio from your radio enters your computer via the sound device where it is converted (demodulated) to digital data for processing by your software. The results are words or images on your computer monitor. When you want to transmit, this same sound device takes the data from your software, such as the words you are typing, and converts it to shifting audio tones according to whatever mode you are using. This conversion is a form of modulation. The tones are then applied to your radio for transmission.

The simplest built-in sound devices are those found in laptops and tablets. They provide two ports to the outside world: microphone (audio input) and headphone (audio output). These are perfectly adequate for HF digital work. Desktop computers often have a similar arrangement, although the output port is usually labeled "speaker." A "line" input may also be included for stronger audio signals. In all cases these ports come in the form of ⅛-inch stereo jacks.

Some desktops computers offer sound cards that plug into the motherboard. These devices are more elaborate. Some sound cards can offer as many as 12 external connections. At the rear of your computer you may find LINE IN, MIC IN, LINE OUT, SPEAKER OUT, PCM OUT, PCM IN, JOYSTICK, FIREWIRE, S/PDIF, REAR CHANNELS, or SURROUND jacks, just to name a few. For HF digital use, the important jacks are MIC or LINE IN and SPEAKER OUT.

Later in this chapter we'll discuss how to connect these sound devices to your radio, but one item needs to be briefly mentioned now: the interface.

As you'll see later, the interface is yet another critical component because it is the link between the computer and the radio. The reason to mention it now is because the trend in interface technology has been to incorporate the sound device into the interface itself. At the time of this writing there are several interfaces by companies such as microHAM, West Mountain Radio, and TigerTronics that feature their own built-in sound devices. These interfaces are extremely convenient because they work independently of whatever sound device you have in your computer. Just plug in their USB cables and you're good to go. It doesn't matter what kind of computer you are using; the interface will work with it. You also avoid a rat's nest of wiring between the computer and the radio.

Whether the sound device is in a plug-in card, a set of chips on the computer motherboard, or a circuit inside an interface, one question often arises: Does the quality of the sound device affect your ability to operate?

This is one of the most common questions among HF digital operators. After all, the sound device is second only to the radio as the most critical link in the performance chain. A poor sound device will bury weak signals in noise of its own making and will potentially distort your transmit audio as well.

Before you dash out to purchase a costly high-end sound card, or obsess over the sound chipset in your interface or on your motherboard, ask yourself an important question: How do you intend to operate? If you have a modest station and intend to enjoy casual chats and a bit of DXing, save your money. An inexpensive sound card, or the sound chipset that is probably on your computer's motherboard or in your interface, is adequate for the task. There is little point in investing in a luxury sound device if you lack the radio or antennas to hear weak signals to begin with, or if they cannot hear you.

On the other hand, if you own the station hardware necessary to be competitive in digital DX hunting or contesting, a good sound card can give you an edge. This is particularly true if you are using a software-defined radio. Sound card performance is critical for this application.

In 2007 the ARRL undertook an evaluation of 11 common sound card models. The study was performed by Jonathan Taylor, K1RFD, and the results were published in the "Product Review" section of the May 2007 issue of *QST*. As you'd expect, the high-end sound cards came out on top, but think carefully before you reach for your wallet. Don't buy more performance than you really need.

Software

When we're talking about putting together a station computer, a brief word about software is in order.

I say "brief" because it isn't practical to discuss software in detail within the pages of a printed book. Software evolves too rapidly for a book that has a useful lifetime measured in years. Any specific details would be obsolete almost before the book left the printing press. Instead, let's talk about software in broad strokes, beginning with operating systems.

As I mentioned earlier, most computers in Amateur Radio stations are running on some form of Microsoft *Windows*. Apple Macintosh owners are obviously quite fond of the various *MacOS* incarnations, which have proven themselves to be efficient and reliable operating systems. The universe of Mac users is growing, but Amateur Radio software titles for the Mac are still few in number.

The *Linux* operating system in its various versions enjoys a loyal following among amateurs who like writing their own software and tinkering at the operating system level. Like the Mac, there is ham software available, but the offerings are somewhat sparse.

The three operating systems have their vocal advocates and I'd be a fool to champion one over another. All have their advantages and disadvantages to consider from an Amateur Radio point of view.

Windows

Pro: Sheer variety. Most Amateur Radio software is written for *Windows,* so you have a rich selection of compatible software to choose from.

Con: Because of the widespread use of *Windows*, it is a favorite target for hackers. Anti-virus software is a must and this can significantly hamper the efficiency of *Windows* and cause other annoying issues. Also, *Windows* can be expensive if purchased and installed separately.

MacOS

Pro: Stability and performance. Highly intuitive and easy to use. Also, hackers have only rarely targeted *MacOS*.

Con: *MacOS* runs only on Apple Macintosh computers. It can be made to run on PCs, but it isn't an exercise for the fainthearted. Amateur Radio software for *MacOS* is limited.

Linux

Pro: Open source and free of charge. Depending on the version, can be quite efficient and powerful. Because there are so many versions in the field, hackers generally don't bother designing viruses for it. They prefer easier prey.

Con: Directory structure and commands may be very different compared to *Windows*. The Amateur Radio software selection is very limited.

Beyond the operating systems, we have specific software for HF digital operating. In the beginning programs were designed for one specific

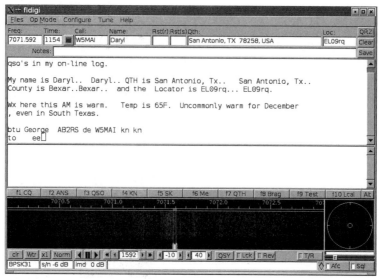

Fldigi multimode software operating PSK31.

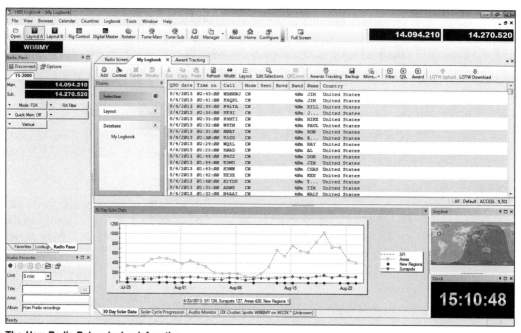

The *Ham Radio Deluxe* logbook function.

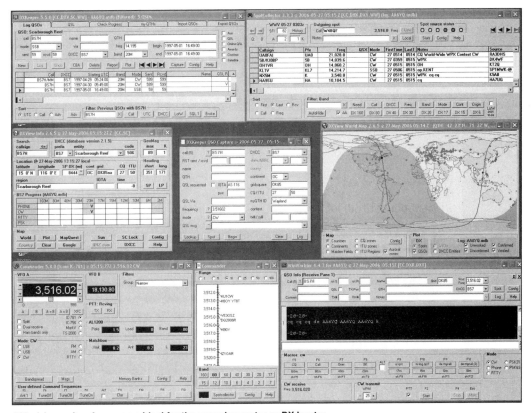

DXLab is a suite of programs ideal for the casual operator or DX hunter.

mode, such as *DigiPan* for PSK31 (**www.digipan.net**) or *MMTTY* for RTTY (**http://hamsoft.ca/pages/mmtty.php**). While mode-specific software still exists, the trend has been strongly in favor of multimode software that can operate many different HF digital modes.

The most popular multimode applications are…

❑ **Windows**
  Ham Radio Deluxe **www.hrdsoftwarellc.com**
  MixW **http://mixw.net**
  MultiPSK **http://f6cte.free.fr/index_anglais.htm**
  Fldigi **www.w1hkj.com/Fldigi.html**

❑ **MacOS**
  Cocoamodem **www.w7ay.net/site/Applications/cocoaModem/**
  Multimode **www.blackcatsystems.com/software/multimode.html**

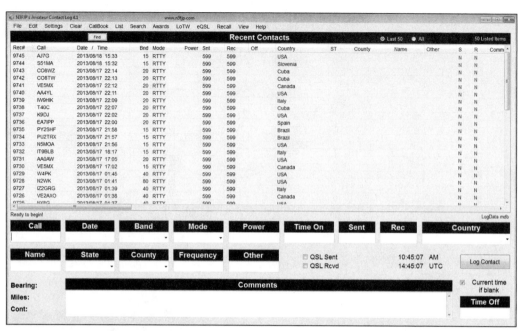

ACIog (Amateur Contact Log) is an inexpensive general-purpose logging program for *Windows*.

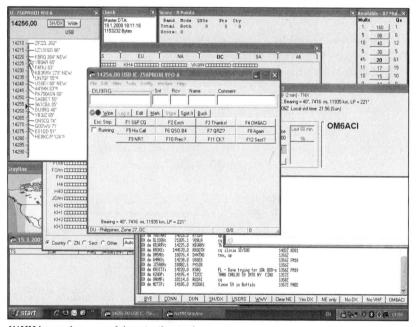

N1MM Logger is a powerful contesting tool.

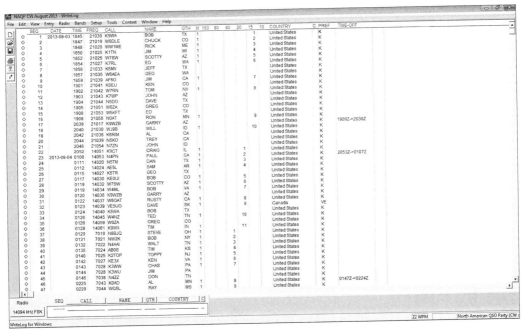

WriteLog is a popular contesting program that includes the ability to send and receive RTTY.

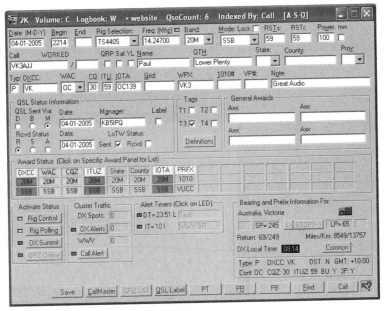

Prolog2K logging software for *Windows*.

❏ **Linux**

Fldigi www.w1hkj.com/Fldigi.html

For logging applications, there are a large number of programs available, including…

❏ *DXLab* **www.dxlabsuite.com**

❏ *ACLog* **www.n3fjp.com**

❏ *Ham Radio Deluxe* (it includes logging among its functions)
www.hrdsoftwarellc.com

❏ *DX4Win* **www.dx4win.com**

❏ *LOGic* **www.hosenose.com**

❏ *MicroLog* **www.wa0h.com**

❏ *ProLog* **www.prologsystem.com**

❏ *MacLoggerDX* **www.dogparksoftware.com/MacLoggerDX.html**

…and a Google search will no doubt uncover many more.

The Interface — the Full Story

At rock bottom an interface for digital operating has only one job to do: to allow the computer to toggle the radio between transmit and receive. It achieves this by using a signal from the computer to switch on a transistor (see **Figure 4.2**). This transistor "conducts" and effectively brings the transceiver's *PTT* (Push to Talk) line to ground potential or very close to it. When the PTT line is grounded, the transceiver switches to transmit. When the signal from the computer disappears, the transistor no longer conducts and the PTT line is electrically elevated above ground. The result is that the transceiver returns to the receive mode.

The signal from the computer appears at a specific pin on a serial (COM) or USB port. Your HF digital software generates the signal when you click your mouse on TRANSMIT or some other button with a similar label.

If an interface can be so straightforward, couldn't you just build your

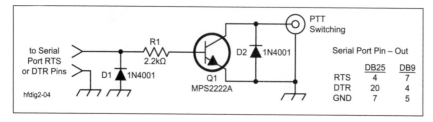

Figure 4.2 — An interface for digital operating allows the computer to toggle the radio between transmit and receive by using a signal from the computer to switch on a transistor.

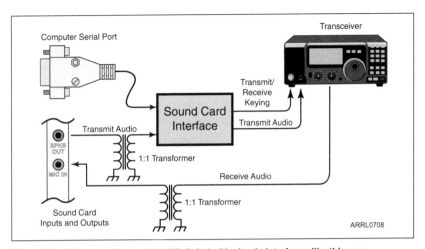

Figure 4.3 — Many amateurs enjoy HF digital with simple interfaces like this one.

own? Yes, you could. Many amateurs enjoy HF digital with simple interfaces like the one shown here. In addition to the switching circuit in Figure 4.2, they connect shielded audio cables between the computer and the radio to carry the transmit and receive audio signals. See **Figure 4.3**.

In Figure 4.3 you'll note that the audio lines include 1:1 isolation transformers. The reason for this is to avoid the dreaded *ground loop*. A ground loop results when current flows in conductors connecting two devices at different electrical potentials. In your HF station the conductors in question are usually the audio cables running between the radio and the computer.

A ground loop typically manifests itself as a hum that you'll hear in your receive audio, or that other stations will hear in your transmit audio. The hum can be so loud it will distort the received or transmitting signals, making digital communication impossible.

The isolation transformers effectively break the ground loop path while still allowing the audio signals to reach their destinations. These

The Rigblaster Advantage interface by West Mountain Radio.

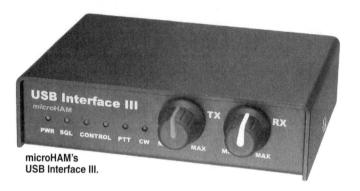

microHAM's
USB Interface III.

transformers are inexpensive, usually selling for less than $3 each from sources such as RadioShack.

To Roll or Not to Roll

There are good reasons to roll your own interface, the cost savings being chief among them. On the other hand, if you purchase an interface off the shelf you'll be able to benefit from enhanced design features, depending on how much you want to pay. The short list of useful features includes …

❑ **Independent Audio Level Controls.** These are knobs on the front panel of the interface that allow you to quickly raise or lower the transmit or receive audio levels. Many amateurs prefer to manage the audio levels in this fashion compared to doing it in software.

❑ **CW keying.** Full-featured interfaces handle more than just HF digital. They can also use keying signals from the computer to send Morse code with a separate connection to the transceiver's CW key jack. This allows you to send CW from your keyboard rather than with a hand key, a useful feature for higher speed CW exchanges during contests.

❑ **FSK keying.** If you want to operate RTTY with the FSK function of your transceiver, assuming your rig offers such a function, the FSK keying feature translates keying signals from your computer into the MARK/SPACE data pulses necessary for FSK RTTY.

❑ **Microphone input.** If you are making HF digital connections to your radio through the microphone jack rather than the rear panel accessory port, you'll need to unplug the interface cable whenever you want to use your microphone for a voice conversation. To make operating more convenient, some interfaces allow you to keep your microphone plugged into the interface at all times, switching between your microphone or computer as necessary.

❏ **Transceiver control.** Remember that a basic interface does not allow your computer to truly control your radio, except in the sense that it can switch your radio between transmit and receive. Deluxe interfaces include the extra circuitry needed to allow full computer control of your transceiver. Sometimes referred to as *CAT* (Computer Aided Transceive), this is a separate function that passes all the available controls from your radio to your computer. Depending on the type of transceiver you own and the software you are using, CAT allows you to change frequency, raise and lower power levels, and much more. If your transceiver has the ability to connect directly to your computer through an RS-232 serial connection, USB cable, or Ethernet port, you don't need the CAT feature. The CAT function is primarily intended for radios that use transistor-transistor (TTL) signals for control. Manufacturers sell their own CAT interfaces, but they tend to be expensive. An interface with CAT functionality brings everything together in one affordable box.

❏ **Built-in Sound Device.** As we discussed earlier, several interface designs include a built-in sound device. This is particularly handy in that it liberates the sound device in your computer for other functions. You can enjoy music on your computer, for example, without having to worry that you are meddling with the sound levels you've set up for HF digital operating. In addition, an interface with a built-in sound device greatly reduces the number of cables connecting the computer and radio. The audio signals, as well as transmit/receive keying functions, are all carried over a single USB cable; there are no connections to your computer's sound ports.

❏ **Pre-Made Cables.** Most commercial interface manufacturers either include cables specifically wired for your radio free of charge, or offer them at an additional cost. This significantly reduces the hassle of wiring your HF digital station.

At the time of this writing, a basic off-the-shelf interface costs about $50; a multi-featured deluxe interface runs as high as $400. You'll need to shop among the manufacturers to find an interface that has the features you desire at a cost you are willing to pay. The most popular interface manufacturers include . . .

microHAM: **www.microham-usa.com**
MFJ: **www.mfjenterprises.com**
TigerTronics: **www.tigertronics.com**
West Mountain Radio: **www.westmountainradio.com**
RigExpert: **www.rigexpert.com**

Putting it all Together

If you've chosen an interface with a built-in sound device, the rest of the assembly is relatively easy. You'll need a set of audio and PTT cables to connect the interface to your transceiver, either at the microphone and headphone jacks, or at the accessory jack. As I've already mentioned, you can purchase this cable from the interface manufacturer or make your own. The USB cable from the interface simply plugs into your computer.

The USB connection to your computer can be a little tricky in one respect, though. When you plug the USB cable into the computer for the first time, the computer may attempt to load and run a *driver* application so it can "talk" to your interface. This driver may already exist on your computer, or you may need to load it from a CD supplied by the manufacturer. Once the driver is loaded, the computer will recognize the interface every time you plug it in thereafter.

Even though the interface is connecting to your computer through a USB cable, it is depending on good old-fashioned serial communication just as though the connection had been made through a COM port. The interface accomplishes this by creating a *virtual COM port* in your computer. In other words, it uses software to emulate the function of a COM port.

Why is it important for you to know this? The answer is that your digital software will need to be configured so that it "knows" which COM port to use for PTT keying, CAT functions, etc. That means you'll need to know this as well!

In *Windows* it is a matter of going to the **Control Panel** and hunting down the **Device Manager** icon. Once you've started Device Manager, click on the **Port** section and you'll see all your computer ports listed in order. Look for a port labeled "USB Serial Port" or "Virtual COM Port" (see **Figure 4.4**). Next to it you'll see a COM number. Write this number down because you'll need to enter it when you're setting up your HF digital program when it asks for the "serial port" or "PTT port" (**Figure 4.5**).

When the computer recognizes the USB interface, it also recognizes the sound device within the interface. It will consider this device as another sound unit, just as though you had installed a second sound card inside the computer. (The computer doesn't know that this sound device is sitting in a box a few feet away and it doesn't care!) Again, this is important to understand because when you set up your software

Figure 4.4 — *Windows* Device Manager with the Ports section expanded. Notice that the USB Serial Port has been assigned COM 11.

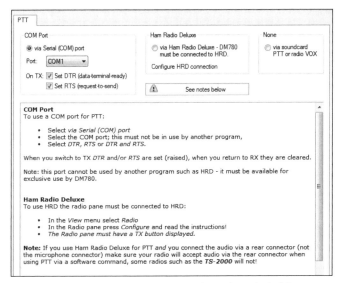

Figure 4.5 — This screen from the *Fldigi* software is typical of those that ask you to select a COM port for your interface (see the upper left corner).

you may need to specify which sound device the software should use. Obviously you will need to select the sound device in your interface. Most software applications have drop-down menus that will list the available sound devices automatically. Don't expect to see your interface device listed by brand name. Instead, it may show up as "USB Sound," "USB Audio Codec" or something similar.

Non-USB Interfaces

If your interface doesn't have a USB connection, it likely uses a traditional serial connection instead. If your computer has a serial (COM) port, you need only attach a serial cable (typically a cable with 9-pin plugs at both ends) between the computer and the interface.

In most computers these serial ports fall in a range between COM 1 and COM 4. Plug your serial cable into an available port and use a bit of trial and error to find out which one you've selected. Start your HF digital program and go to the configuration menu. Enter a "1" into the COM port selection box and then click on the TRANSMIT button in your software. If your transceiver goes into transmit, congratulations — you've found the correct COM port. If not, try 2, 3, 4, etc.

Managing the Audio Connections

If you own an interface with a built-in sound device, you'll need to connect the transmit and receive audio cables between the interface and the transceiver, either at the microphone and headphone jacks, or at the accessory jack. If your interface is of the simple transmit/receive switching variety, one or both sets of audio cables may have to go all the way back to the computer.

Even though you're using shielded audio cables, there is the potential for trouble when RF is in the air. This is especially true when your station

antenna is close to your operating position. The audio cables can act like antennas themselves, picking up RF and wreaking havoc on your station. I've seen some instances where the computer shut down or reset whenever the transceiver was keyed. In other examples the RF energy mixed with the transmit audio and resulted in a horrendously distorted output.

If you suspect you have an RF interference problem in your HF digital station, you can diagnose it by reducing your output power and observing the results. If 100 W output gives you grief but 50 W is smooth as silk, you clearly have an RF interference issue.

Presumably you've kept your audio cables as short as possible. Stringing up 20-foot-long audio cables between the radio, the interface, and the computer is just asking for trouble.

But if your audio cables are of reasonable length and you still suffer interference, it is time to buy some *toroid cores*. These are circular donuts made of a powdered iron and epoxy mixture. They come in various sizes and are rated for suppression at various frequencies. For HF applications, Type 61 toroids are among the most effective. To suppress RF on an audio cable, wrap the cable through the toroid at least 10 times with evenly spaced turns.

With the right toroid in the right place, you can greatly reduce or eliminate RF interference. For severe cases you may need to place a toroid on every cable.

You'll often see used toroids for sale at hamfest fleamarkets, but don't buy a used toroid unless you know the type of material it contains. When in doubt, buy toroids new from manufacturers such as Amidon at **www.amidoncorp.com**. Avoid snap-on ferrite cores. While they are certainly easy to use, they are not as effective as toroids that you wind yourself.

Setting Up the Transceiver

Much of the advice that follows depends on what sort of transceiver you own and what kind of interface you are using to create your HF digital setup. When in doubt, always consult your transceiver and interface manuals.

If your interface is connecting to the radio through the transceiver accessory port, see if there is a function in the transceiver to adjust the accessory audio input and output levels. If it exists, this is a convenient way to establish "baseline" audio levels for the radio. Of course, you can also adjust audio levels at your computer and possibly at your interface (depending on the kind of interface you purchase). If it seems as though you aren't getting enough audio from the radio, or if it seems that you can't drive the radio to full output regardless of the computer or interface settings, check these transceiver settings as well.

Audio Overdrive

Speaking of driving rigs to full output, we need to discuss the danger of audio overdrive. Without question this is one of the most common issues among new HF digital operators.

Regardless of the type of digital mode you enjoy, there is an almost instinctual tendency among new operators to adjust their transmit audio levels while only watching their transceiver's RF output meter. They place their radios into the transmit mode and crank up the audio levels at their computer or interfaces until they see a satisfying 100 W RF output. At that point they assume they are finished and ready to take to the airwaves. This is known as "tuning for maximum smoke."

They could not be more mistaken!

First of all, most HF digital modes do not require 100 W of power to make contacts. One of the benefits of HF digital, in fact, is that you can make contacts at surprisingly low power levels. For some digital modes such as JT65, 100 W output is considered obscene!

But most importantly, adjusting for full RF output ignores the fact that you may be grossly overdriving your radio to achieve your satisfaction. The result is often a wildly distorted signal that's not only difficult to decode, it splatters across the band, ruining every conversation in its wake. The ham who insists on generating a hideous signal for the sake of a few extra watts is known in traditional parlance as a LID. (No, it isn't a term of endearment.)

Rather than gazing at the transceiver meter as it displays your RF output, switch the meter to monitor *ALC* (Automatic Limiting Control) instead. All transceivers display ALC activity differently. The display may simply indicate the presence and amount of transmit audio limiting taking place. Other displays may include a "safe zone." If the ALC activity remains within

In this example, notice that the transmit audio has been adjusted to keep the meter needle from going beyond the ALC "safe zone" (bottom left portion of the meter scale).

the safe zone, your transmit audio levels are acceptable.

When you transmit a test signal, do not increase the audio level beyond the ALC safe zone, or beyond the point where ALC activity is excessive. When you see the needle or LEDs swing hard to the right, this is a warning that you are supplying way too much audio to the radio and that the ALC circuit is trying to rein you in.

The goal is to generate the desired RF output while keeping ALC activity to a minimum (or even zero), or while keeping the ALC meter in the safe zone. It is important to keep in mind that minimal ALC activity does *not* necessarily guarantee a clean signal. It does in many instances, but your best insurance is to ask for reports whenever you are in doubt. If someone reports that you are splattering, reduce the transmit audio level until they say your signal is clean. Note this setting so that you can return to it again easily.

Squelching Those Computer Sounds

When you begin listening to HF digital signals, don't be surprised if you occasionally hear beeps, dings, chimes, or a disembodied voice declaring "You've got mail!"

Most of this interference isn't deliberate. It is caused by VOX-type interfaces that key transceivers whenever they detect audio — *any audio* — from the computers. I'm willing to bet the operators aren't even aware that their computers are guilty of this obnoxious behavior.

The solution, at least in *Windows*, is simple: Turn off "*Windows* sounds" before you get on the air. You can also do this manually by opening *Window's* **Control Panel** and double-clicking the **Sound and Audio Devices** icon. Click the Sound tab, and under Sound Schemes select **No Sounds**. (Depending on the *Windows* version in question, the labels may differ.) Your fellow hams will thank you!

CAT Communication

If your software and interface support full transceiver control (CAT), you'll need to make sure that the data communication rates between the interface or computer and the transceiver are the same. Some clever pieces of CAT software will automatically analyze the data from the transceiver and quickly determine the data rate. For others, you'll have to enter a menu and specify the data rate.

In most CAT-capable radios you'll find a menu setting that will allow you to specify a data rate, often expressed as "baud." A rate of 9600 baud, for example, is common. You may need to access this menu to find out what setting the radio is currently using, or to change the radio's data rate to something the interface or software can handle.

Chapter 5

Station Accessories

When planning your HF station it's easy to become fixated on the big stuff: antennas, transceivers, amplifiers, and computers. But don't neglect the little things, the accessories that play a large role in making your station effective and fun to operate.

Microphones and Headsets

Your HF transceiver will likely include its own microphone, but these are usually handheld mics. A handheld microphone is perfectly fine for most of the operating you are likely to do. However, if you think you'll be doing a lot of voice operating — contesting, DXing and net operations come to mind — you may want to consider a more appropriate microphone for the job.

Mike Braun, KB8ZYE, keeps his hands free while operating a Voice of America special event station by using a microphone mounted on an articulated boom.

The Icom SM-30 desk microphone.

There is a good chance your HF transceiver included a basic handheld microphone like the one shown here. These microphones are good for casual operating.

A headset microphone is yet another approach to hands-free operating, with the advantage of bringing the audio directly to your ears. Headsets are often the microphones of choice among contesters.

A foot switch like this one can be used to key your radio when coupled with a headset or boom-mounted microphone.

Sound quality is critical to being understood on the air, so it makes sense to invest in a higher-quality microphone. Heil Sound (**www.heil-sound.com**) is perhaps the most well-known microphone manufacturer in the Amateur Radio community. Their microphones are not inexpensive, but they can make a substantial difference in how well you come across, especially under challenging conditions. You'll find comparable microphones from other manufacturers as well, including the company that made your transceiver.

The trick to making the best use of a microphone is keeping it out of your way. That's one of the drawbacks of handheld and even standard desk microphones. They occupy valuable real estate on your desk and they require the use of at least one of your hands to operate. The solution for many amateurs is to emulate the professionals by placing the microphone on an articulated boom that can be positioned above the desk and directly in front of your face. These booms are commonly available, or you can even make your own. They typically feature clamps that attach the base of the boom to one side of your desk. By using a foot switch (another valuable accessory item) you can key your transceiver without lifting a finger — your hands will be completely free.

An alternative to the boom mic is the microphone headset. This device combines the microphone element and headphones into a single unit. Many hams consider headsets ideal for speaking and hearing clearly while keeping their hands free. Headsets are especially prized by contest operators who must keep their hands free at all times. Again, you can use a footswitch to key your rig, or use the VOX function to key the radio when you speak.

Speakers

Surely your transceiver will have a speaker included in the enclosure, so why you would you want to consider a separate, external speaker? The answer is that transceiver speakers are usually quite small and the audio quality can suffer substantially as a result. If you doubt this, try plugging a sizeable speaker into the transceiver's headphone jack and listen to the results. You'll probably be astonished.

This station speaker includes a built-in audio amplifier and DSP filtering.

This Kenwood station speaker is designed to match several Kenwood transceivers.

Unfortunately, not all HF transceivers have ports for external speakers. If your chosen rig doesn't, consider tapping the audio at the rear panel accessory jack and feeding it to an external audio amplifier. This audio is often at a constant level, which is perfect for applying to an amplifier. From the amplifier you can drive a large speaker and adjust the audio to a comfortable level. The downside, however, is that your transmitted signal may show up as a loud buzz in the speakers. If so, you may need to apply some RF suppression techniques (such as wrapping the speaker wires several times through a ferrite core).

You may find external speakers offered by the company that made your transceiver. Most of these are styled to match your radio. You'll also find external speakers made by third party manufacturers. The more deluxe models include built-in audio amplifiers and even DSP audio filtering. Check the advertising pages of *QST* magazine.

CW Keys

If you're going to join the thousands of amateurs who enjoy operating CW on the HF bands, you're going to need a key. The most basic type is the *straight key*, and it is as old as Morse code itself. Learning to use a straight key proficiently isn't easy; it takes practice to send smooth CW. Most hams can send up to 15 WPM with a straight key, although some can send at much higher speeds.

The most popular method of sending CW is with the *electronic keyer*. This usually consists of a set of finely balanced switches known as *paddles*. Hams who've mastered electronic keyers can send CW at astonishingly high

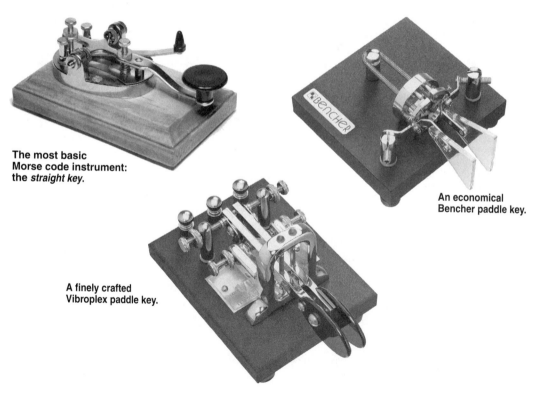

The most basic
Morse code instrument:
the *straight key*.

An economical
Bencher paddle key.

A finely crafted
Vibroplex paddle key.

speeds. It is fascinating to watch their fingers dance on the paddles!

The paddles are connected to the electronic keyer, which automatically generates dits and dahs depending on which paddle you touch. If you touch the dah paddle, for example, the keyer will send a string of dahs until you release the pressure; touch the dit paddle and dits are sent. To send the letter "Q," you'd touch the dah paddle just long enough for the keyer to send two dahs, touch the dit paddle just once, and then finally touch the dah paddle again to send the last dah: *dah-dah-dit-dah*. The keyer has an adjustment so that you can select the sending speed you desire.

Many modern transceivers have electronic keyers built in. If your radio doesn't include this feature, you can purchase an external keyer.

It is also possible to send CW with a computer keyboard. This is anathema to CW purists, though, and is usually only done by hams involved in contests where the same information is sent repeatedly. If you want to send CW in this fashion, your contest software may be able to do it through an interface as we discussed in Chapter 4. You can also download free software such as *CWType* (**www.dxsoft.com/en/products/cwtype/**) to perform this function.

Test Equipment

Your first HF station will require little, if any, test equipment, but it is a good idea to have a few items on your shopping list just the same. The most critical piece of test gear is an SWR/power meter. You'll need one of these to determine whether your antenna system is properly matched to your transceiver. This meter will also display the RF output level of the radio.

Most transceivers have SWR/power metering built in. If your station setup requires an antenna tuner, many of these include SWR/power metering as well. But if you don't have a meter in either your transceiver or tuner, I'd strongly recommend purchasing one for your station.

Even if your transceiver or tuner already has an SWR/power meter, a separate meter is still a nice thing to have at hand. You never know when you might need to take it outside, for example, to troubleshoot an antenna problem.

The same is true for another piece of gear that isn't strictly necessary, but awfully useful from time to time: the *dummy load*. A dummy

An MFJ SWR/power meter.

HB9EFY built this "can style" dummy load.

This is an example of a dummy load that uses a large heat sink to keep cool.

If you enjoy experimenting with antennas, an antenna analyzer is one of the most useful pieces of test equipment you can own.

load is little more than a 50 Ω resistor in a shielded container. These loads are designed to simulate the impedance of an antenna while radiating very little RF, and they come in various power ratings. The high power dummy loads include fans and/or cooling fluids to dissipate heat.

Dummy loads are excellent tools when you need to diagnose a problem with your radio or antenna system. Let's say you suddenly notice that your antenna system SWR has gone sky high. Is the problem at the antenna, or somewhere in between? You can answer that question right away by disconnecting the coaxial cable at the antenna and attaching the dummy load. If the SWR goes back to normal, you know you have a faulty antenna. If it doesn't, your antenna is okay but a problem exists somewhere in the cable between the dummy load and your radio.

If you anticipate experimenting with antennas, another worthwhile investment is an *antenna analyzer*. This device is essentially a low power transmitter coupled to a microprocessor-based RF analyzer. While it may set you back $200 or more, it is difficult to name a more important device for antenna experimentation. With an antenna analyzer you can instantly determine the resonant frequency of your antenna and adjust it accordingly.

Not only will an analyzer tell you the impedance and SWR of an antenna system at a given frequency, you can also use it to determine useful information such as transmission line loss. Anyone who owns an analyzer will tell you that they can't imagine living without it.

World Map

It may seem silly, but you'd be surprised at how many hams neglect to purchase something as simple as a map. A good Amateur Radio map supplies a wealth of information at a glance. You'll see all the current DX Century Club entities, along with their call sign prefixes, as well as the borders of CQ zones and ITU zones — information of vital importance to DXers and contesters. If your station includes directional, rotatable antennas, an

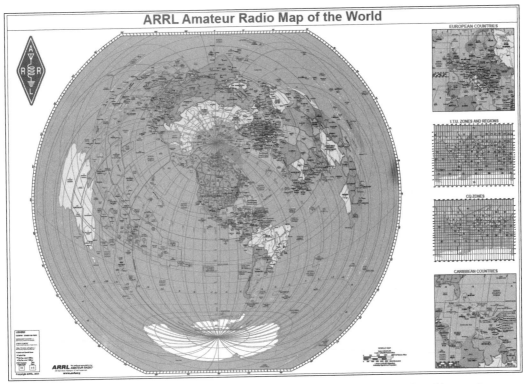

This is an *azimuthal projection* Amateur Radio map centered on the United States. Not only does this map show the locations and call sign prefixes of all DXCC entities, it shows you the proper direction to point your antenna. You can purchase this map, and others, from the ARRL online store at www.arrl.org/shop.

azimuthal projection map will help you determine where to point your beams to contact a particular area of the world. The ARRL sells several large, laminated Amateur Radio maps that are ideal for any station. You'll find them online at **www.arrl.org/shop**.

Station Clock

Yet another silly item, right? Not really. Every station needs a large, easy-to-read clock that can display time in the 24-hour format (what some people call the "military time"). This is because the Amateur Radio standard for timekeeping is 24-hour format *Coordinated Universal Time*.

The official abbreviation for Coordinated Universal Time is *UTC*. This abbreviation arose from a desire by the International Telecommunication Union and the International Astronomical Union to use the same abbreviation in all languages. English speakers originally proposed *CUT* (for "coordinated universal time"), while French speakers proposed *TUC* (for "temps universal coordonné"). The compromise that emerged was *UTC*.

Although it is certainly impressive, your UTC station clock doesn't need to be this fancy. Any clock that can display "24-hour time" will do.

UTC is actually a global timekeeping standard in many fields, not just Amateur Radio. The aviation industry, for example, relies on UTC.

The point of UTC is to establish a single time reference that everyone can agree upon, no matter where they are located. The time in any given time zone is either a positive or negative offset of UTC. For American amateurs, the following time zone offsets apply:

Time Zone	Hours Behind UTC
Eastern	5
Central	6
Mountain	7
Pacific	8
Alaska	9
Hawaii	10

For example, 2300 UTC is 1800 Eastern Time (UTC — 5 = Eastern Time). Of course, if your area observes Daylight Saving Time, you'll have to subtract one hour from the offset during those months.

As you can probably guess, figuring out the correct UTC time by adding the proper offset to your local time is inconvenient and prone to error. That's why it makes sense to have a UTC station clock. Once you set your station clock to UTC, you'll never have to guess or calculate again. When it is time to log a contact or fill out a QSL card, just glance at your UTC station clock and you'll always know the correct UTC time. Best of all, UTC never changes. You may have to change your household clock to adjust for Daylight Saving Time, but your UTC station clock will never need to be reset.

Station Log

While the FCC no longer requires you to document every contact in a station log, it is still a good idea to have a log on hand and keep it up to date. A log charts your progress toward various awards. Beyond award chasing, however, a log is your radio diary, a reflection of your journey in the hobby. It is particularly interesting to leaf through a logbook that you've kept for several years, savoring the memories of contacts gone by.

The ARRL 8½ x 11 logbook.

Logs have a practical side as well. Let's say a neighbor comes knocking and accuses you of interfering with his TV last night during the NBA championship game. Assuming that you're innocent, you can show your log and prove that you weren't on the radio at that time. Logs are also handy for keeping notes about your station, such as antenna SWR measurements, transceiver output power and more.

As we discussed earlier in this book, many amateurs rely on logging software. However, you can just as easily use a paper log. In fact, the ARRL offers an 8½ × 11 spiral bound logbook as well as a small "mini" logbook. You'll find both at the ARRL online store at **www. arrl.org/shop**.

Chapter 6

Power –
For Better or Worse

We begin with power — the kind you *want*. You need electricity in abundance to power everything from radios to test equipment.

If your station is located in a room with electrical outlets, you're in luck. If your station is located in the basement, an attic or other area without a convenient 120-V source, you may need to run a new line to your operating position. Unless you are a licensed electrician, this is a job best left to the professionals.

If you are considering a high-power amplifier for your station — now or in the future — invest in a 240 Vac line for your station room in addition to the 120-V supply. Yes, you'll find amplifiers that can be powered from 120 V, but they require current levels that may exceed the limits of standard house wiring. To avoid overloading the circuit and to reduce household light dimming or blinking when the amplifier is in use, and for the best possible voltage regulation in the equipment, you're better off installing a separate 240-V line with an appropriate current rating.

Even if you don't intend to use an amplifier, keep in mind that the usual circuits feeding household outlets are rated at 15 or 20 A. This may or may not be enough current to power your station. Check the VA (volt-amp) ratings for each piece of gear. Usually, the manufacturer will specify the required current at 120 V; if the power consumption is rated in watts, divide that rating by 120 V to get amperes. Modern switching power supplies draw more current as the line voltage drops, so if your line voltage is markedly lower than 120 V, you need to take that into account. Note that the code requires you to use the "nameplate"

An ac power strip with a built-in surge protector.

Kill-A-Watt meters by P3 International (www. p3international.com) measure volts, amps, VA and power factor

current, even if you've measured the actual current, and it's less. If the total current required is near 80% of the circuit's rating (12 A on a 15-A circuit or 16 A on a 20-A circuit), you need to install another circuit. Keep in mind that other rooms may be powered from the same branch of the electrical system, so the power consumption of any equipment connected to other outlets on the branch must be taken into account. If you would like to measure just how much power your equipment consumes, the inexpensive Kill-A-Watt meters by P3 International (**www. p3international.com**) measure volts, amps, VA and power factor.

Connecting and Disconnecting Power

Something that is often overlooked is the need to have a way to safely and quickly disconnect all power to every device in your station. This includes not only the ac power, but also battery banks, solar panels, and uninterruptible power supplies (UPS). Most hams won't have the luxury of a dedicated room with a dedicated power feed and the "big red switch" on the wall, so you'll have several switches and cords that would need to be disconnected. The realities of today's ham stations, with computers, multiple wall transformers, network interfaces, and the radio equipment itself makes this tricky to do.

One convenient means is a switched outlet strip, as used for computer equipment, if you have a limited number of devices. If you need more switched outlets, you can control multiple low-voltage controlled switched outlets from a common source. Or you can build or buy a portable power distribution box similar to those used on construction sites or stage sets; they are basically a portable subpanel with individual circuit breakers for each receptacle, and fed by a suitable cord or extension cord. No matter what scheme you use, however, it's important that it be labeled so that someone else will know how to turn off the power if you are unavailable.

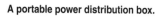

A portable power distribution box.

Lightning Protection

And now we must talk about the kind of power you *don't* want anywhere near your station — the kind that strikes somewhere on our planet every second of every day. With millions of volts and a temperature four times greater than the surface of the Sun, lightning is a force to be reckoned with.

As amateurs it may sometimes seem as though we go out of our way to tempt lightning. Who else would dare hang long wires within the branches of tall trees, or erect metal towers that reach to the sky? Hams have a "special relationship" with lightning, but it shouldn't keep you from enjoying your station, even if you live in area that gets more than its fair share of strikes (such as Florida). A few common-sense measures will go a long way to keeping you and your station as safe as possible.

Lightning doesn't have to strike your antenna to cause damage. A strike on a nearby power line is more than sufficient to send a powerful surge into your home.

This used to be a 2 meter antenna — until it took a blast from Mother Nature!

Towers

Because a tower is usually the highest metal object on the property, it is the primary strike target. Proper tower grounding is essential to lightning protection. The goal is to establish short multiple paths to the Earth so that the strike energy is divided and dissipated.

Connect each tower leg and each fan of metal guy wires to a separate ground rod. Space the rods at least 6 feet apart. Bond the leg ground rods together with #6 AWG or larger copper bonding conductor (form a ring around the tower base). Connect a continuous bonding conductor between the tower ring ground and the entrance panel. Make all connections with fittings approved for grounding applications. Do not use solder for these connections. Solder will be destroyed in the heat of a lightning strike. Because galvanized steel (which has a zinc coating) reacts with copper when combined with moisture, use stainless steel hardware between the galvanized metal and the copper grounding materials.

To prevent strike energy from entering your home via the feed line, ground the feed line outside the home. Ground the coax shield to the tower at the antenna and the base to keep the tower and line at the same potential. Several companies offer grounding blocks that make this job easy. All grounding media at the home must be bonded together. This includes lightning protection conductors, electrical service, telephone, antenna system grounds, and underground metal pipes. Any ground rods used for lightning protection or entrance-panel grounding should be spaced at least 6 feet from each other and the electrical service or other utility grounds and then bonded to the ac system ground.

A Cable Entrance Panel

Whether or not you own a tower, the basic concept with lightning protection is to make sure that the radio and other equipment is tied together and "moves together" in the presence of a transient voltage (a high voltage spike caused by a lightning strike). It's not so important that the shack be at "ground" potential, but rather that everything is at the same potential. For fast rise-time transients such as the individual strokes that make up a lightning strike, even a short wire has enough inductance that the voltage drop along the wire is significant. So whether you are on the ground floor or the 10th floor of a building, your station is "far" from Earth potential.

The easiest way to ensure that everything is at the same potential is to tie all the signals to a common reference. In commercial facilities, this reference would be provided by a grid of large diameter cables under the

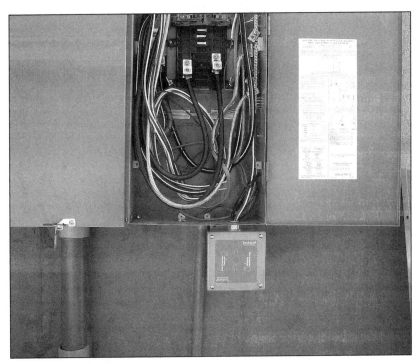

A typical cable entrance panel.

floor, or by wide copper bars, or even a solid metal floor.

A more practical approach for ham stations is to have a single "tie point" for all the signals. This is often, but erroneously, called "single-point ground," but what's really important is that all signal wires — not just the shields — are referenced to that common potential. We want to control the flow of the energy in a strike and eliminate any possible paths for surges to enter the building. This involves routing the feed lines, rotator control cables, and so on at least six feet away from other nearby grounded metal objects.

A commonly-used approach to ensuring that all the connections are tied together is to route all the signals through a single "entrance panel" that will serve as the "single point ground," although it may not actually be at ground potential. A convenient approach is to use a standard electrical box installed in the exterior wall. Both balanced line and coax arrestors should be mounted to a secure ground connection on the outside of the building. The easiest way to do this is to install a large metal enclosure or a metal panel as a bulkhead and grounding block. The panel should be connected to the lightning dissipation ground with a short wide conductor (for minimum impedance), and, like all grounds, bonded to the electrical system's ground. Mount all protective devices, switches, and relay disconnects on the outside facing wall of the bulkhead. The enclosure or panel should be installed in a way that if lightning currents cause a component to fail, the molten metal and flaming debris do not start a fire.

Every conductor that enters the structure, including antenna system control lines, should have its own surge suppressor on an entrance panel. Suppressors are available from a number of manufacturers, including PolyPhaser, as well as the usual electrical equipment suppliers such as Square-D.

Lightning Arrestors

Feed line lightning arrestors are available for both coax cable and balanced line. Most of the balanced line arrestors use a simple spark gap arrangement. DC blocking arrestors for coaxial cable have a fixed frequency range. They present a high impedance to lightning while offering a low impedance to RF.

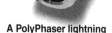

DC continuity arrestors (gas tubes and spark gaps) can be used over a wider frequency range than those that block dc. Where the coax carries supply voltages to remote devices (such as a mast-mounted preamp or remote antenna tuner), dc continuous arrestors must be used.

Note that a lightning arrestor needs to be connected to a nearby ground (such as a ground rod driven into the soil) so that it can dissipate the excessive voltages that appear on your antenna and feed line. When a thunderstorm is overhead, you can occasionally hear a frying noise coming from the arrestor as it does its job.

A PolyPhaser lightning arrester.

The Easiest, Economical Approach

The tips provided in this chapter will go a long way toward helping you avoid lightning damage, but they aren't practical for everyone. If you live in an apartment or rented house, the landlord will probably not allow you to install a cable entrance panel, for example. Or your home design may not allow you to install the kind of lightning protection we've discussed.

Regardless of what you do, nothing will *prevent* a lightning strike. If lightning is going to strike your antenna system, or a point nearby, nothing can stop that from happening. The best you can do is to take steps to prevent or minimize damage.

The easiest, economical approach is the common-sense one: If severe weather threatens, disconnect your transceiver from your antenna and place the cable several feet away from the radio. However, this step by itself will not protect the radio in all circumstances. Lightning may strike a nearby utility line, sending a surge into your house wiring and straight to your radio's ac line, or into the ac line of another piece of gear that is connected to your radio (such as a computer). The only way to be absolutely sure is to disconnect the transceiver from the antenna, the ac line, and all other devices.

In areas that are particularly lightning-prone, some amateurs leave their equipment completely disconnected at all times — not just the antenna cables, but the ac lines as well. When they want to get on the air, it takes only a few minutes to plug everything back in.

If you'd like to learn more about lightning protection, PolyPhaser has an excellent collection of downloadable articles at **www.protectiongroup. com/Utility/Knowledge-Base**.

Operating Awards

Awards hunting is a significant part of the life support system of Amateur Radio operating. It's a major motivating force behind many of the contacts that occur on the bands day after day. It takes skillful operating to qualify, and the reward of having a beautiful certificate or plaque on your ham shack wall commemorating your achievement is very gratifying. If you've been on the air for a while, you can probably get a good start by pulling out your shoebox of QSLs on a cold, winter afternoon to see what gems you already have on hand.

Aside from expanding your Amateur Radio-related knowledge, chasing awards is also a fascinating way to learn about the geography, history, or political structure of another country, or perhaps even your own.

Award Basics

There are some basic considerations to keep in mind when applying for awards. Always carefully read the rules, so that your application complies fully. Use the standard award application if possible. Make sure your application is neat and legible, and that it indicates clearly what you are applying for. Official rules and application materials are available directly from the organization sponsoring the particular award. You can often find the needed information and forms on the web. If you need to get something by postal mail, always include an SASE (self-addressed, stamped envelope) or, in the case of international awards, a self-addressed envelope with IRCs (International Reply Coupons, available from your local Post Office) when making such requests. Sufficient return postage should also be included when directing awards-related correspondence to Awards Managers. Many (if not most) are volunteers. Above all, be patient!

If QSL cards are required with your application, send them the safest possible way and always include sufficient return postage for their return the same way. It is vital that you check your cards carefully before mailing them. Make sure each card contains your call sign and other substantiating information

Hams enjoy exchanging QSL cards and collecting them to count for various awards. Whether you're chasing DX countries, US states, grid locators, call sign prefixes or counties, the QSL card is the foundation, upon which most awards are based. In recent years, hams have gravitated toward ARRL's electronic Logbook of The World to help bolster DXCC and WAS totals, but everyone loves to receive a colorful QSL card in the mail from a "rare one."

(band, mode, and so on). Never send cards that are altered or have information crossed out and marked over, even if such modifications are made by the amateur filling out the card. Altered cards, even if such alterations are made in "good faith," are not acceptable for awards. If you are unsure about a particular card, don't submit it. Secure a replacement.

None of the above is meant to diminish your enthusiasm for awards hunting. These are just helpful hints to make things even more fun for all concerned. Chasing awards is a robust facet of hamming that makes each and every QSO a key element in your present or future Amateur Radio success.

ARRL Awards

To make Amateur Radio QSOs more enjoyable and to add challenge, the League sponsors awards for operating achievement, some of which are the most popular awards in ham radio. Except for the Code Proficiency awards, US applicants must be League members to apply. It is advisable to always check the current fee schedule. Complete information and current fees for all of the ARRL awards described here may be found online at **www.arrl.org/awards**.

First Contact Award

This handsome certificate commemorates that special first on-the-air contact. To give a new ham this special recognition, visit **www.arrl.org/ first-contact** and fill in the contact details (call signs, date, time, band, mode, and so on). Submit the information online and ARRL will send you a certificate completed with the contact information that you provided. There's a place for you to sign and date when presenting the award.

Code Proficiency Certificate

You don't have to be a ham to earn this one. But you do have to copy one of the W1AW qualifying runs. (The current W1AW operating schedule is printed periodically in *QST* and listed on **www.**

The American Radio Relay League, Inc.
Headquarters, Newington, CT USA

Certificate of Code Proficiency

By this certificate and any appended endorsements to show additional qualifications, the
American Radio Relay League expresses recognition of merit and progress in code proficiency on the part of

who has on this date demonstrated skill in the basic art of
reception by ear of the International Morse or Continental
Code. Our examination of copy submitted indicates absolute
accuracy at a speed of _____ words per minute for a period
of at least one minute of plain-language computer generated text averaging five characters to the word,
which we hereby certify. Date of the ARRL transmission from W1AW, _____

Endorsement
here

W5JBP
PRESIDENT

arrl.org/w1aw.) Twice a month, five minutes worth of text is transmitted at the following speeds: 10-15-20-25-30-35 WPM. For a real challenge, W1AW transmits 40 WPM four times a year.

To qualify at any speed, just copy one minute solid. Your copy can be written, printed, or typed. Underline the minute you believe you copied perfectly and send this text to ARRL HQ along with your name, call (if licensed) and complete mailing address, along with the appropriate fee. Your copy is checked directly against the official W1AW transmission copy, and you'll be advised promptly if you've passed or failed. If the news is good, you'll soon receive either your initial certificate or an appropriate endorsement sticker. Check **www.arrl. org/code-proficiency-certificate** for the current fee schedule.

Worked All States (WAS)

The Worked All States (WAS) award is available to all amateurs worldwide who submit proof of having contacted each of the 50 United States. The WAS program includes 10 different awards for working all states on various bands and modes, as well as endorsement stickers for working various kinds of stations.

To earn the basic WAS award, establish two-way communication on the amateur bands with each state. There is no minimum signal report required. Any or all modes and amateur bands (except 60 meters) may be used for general WAS. The District of Columbia may be counted for Maryland.

Contacts must all be made from the same location, or from locations no two of which are more than 50 miles apart. Club station applicants must include the club name and call sign of the club station (or trustee).

Contacts may be made over any period of years. Contacts must be confirmed in writing, preferably in the form of QSL cards. Original confirmations must be submitted (no photocopies). Confirmations must show your call and indicate that two-way communication was established. Specialty awards and endorsements must be shown as two-way (2×) on that band and/or mode. Contacts made with Alaska must be dated January 3, 1959 or later, and with Hawaii dated August 21, 1959 or after.

ARRL's online Logbook of the World (LoTW) also supports the WAS program. If you are an LoTW participant, you can upload your logs and track your progress on various WAS awards and endorsements. When you have gathered the LoTW confirmations needed for an award, you can even apply online. Details on LoTW are given later in this chapter.

Specialty awards (numbered separately) are available for OSCAR Satellite, SSTV, 432 MHz, 222 MHz, 144 MHz, 50 MHz, and 160 meters. The Digital award, issued for working any digital mode (PSK31, AMTOR, PACTOR, RTTY, G-TOR and so forth) is also available. The Digital and Phone awards are dated but not numbered, except RTTY.

Endorsement stickers for the basic mixed mode/band award and any of the specialty awards are available for CW, Novice, QRP, Packet, EME, and any single band. The Novice endorsement is available for the applicant who has worked all states as a Novice licensee. QRP is defined as 5 W output as used by the applicant (the station you work does not need to be running QRP as well), and is affirmed by signature of the applicant on the application.

Contacts made through "repeater" devices or any other power relay method cannot be used for WAS confirmation. (A separate WAS is available for OSCAR satellite contacts.) All stations contacted must be "land stations." Contact with ships (anchored or otherwise) and aircraft cannot be counted. The only exception is permanently docked exhibition ships, such as the Queen Mary and other historic ships. Those are considered land-based in the state where they are docked.

All US applicants must be ARRL members to participate in the WAS program. DX stations are exempt from this requirement.

HQ reserves the right to "spot call" for inspection of cards (at ARRL expense) of applications verified by an HF Awards Manager. The purpose of this is not to question the integrity of any individual, but rather to ensure the overall integrity of the program. More difficult-to-be-attained specialty awards (222 MHz WAS, for example) are more likely to be so called. Failure of the applicant to respond to such a spot check will result in non-issuance of the WAS certificate.

Disqualification: False statements on the WAS application or submission of forged or altered cards may result in disqualification. ARRL does not attempt to determine who has altered a submitted card; therefore do not submit any marked-over cards. The decision of the ARRL Awards Committee in such cases is final.

Application Procedure (please follow carefully): Confirmations (QSLs) and application form may be submitted to an approved ARRL Special Services Club HF Awards Manager for checking. If you can have your application verified locally, you need not submit your cards to HQ. If you cannot have your application verified locally, send your application, cards, and required fees to HQ, as indicated on the application form. You can search for the nearest ARRL HF Awards Manager (Card Checker) by following the link from **www.arrl.org/was**.

Forms and the latest rules for WAS are available online at **www.arrl.org/was**. Be sure that when cards are presented for verification (either locally or to HQ) they are sorted alphabetically by state, as listed on the back of the application form.

All QSL cards sent to HQ must be accompanied by sufficient postage for their safe return, and the required fee (see **www.arrl.org/was**). A WAS pin is available along with the certificate.

Five-Band WAS (5BWAS)

This award is designed to foster more uniform activity throughout the bands, encourage the development of better antennas, and generally offer a challenge to both newcomers and veterans. The basic WAS rules apply, including cards being checked in the field by HF Awards Managers. In addition, 5BWAS carries a start date of January 1, 1970, and contacts before that do not count. Unlike WAS, 5BWAS is a one-time-only award; no band/mode endorsements are available. Contacts made on 1.8, 5, 10, 18, and 24 MHz are not valid for 5BWAS. Forms and the latest rules for WAS are available online at **www.arrl.org/was**.

All QSL cards sent to HQ must be accompanied by sufficient postage for their safe return,

The American Radio Relay League recognizes that

W1HQ

CW   PHONE

has confirmed, via Logbook of the World, two-way communication with stations in each of the fifty states of the United States of America on each of the three operating modes: CW, Phone and Digital.

ARRL Worked All States

President, ARRL

and the required fee (see **www.arrl. org/was**). A special 5BWAS pin and 5BWAS plaque are also available.

Triple Play WAS

The Triple Play WAS (Worked All States) Award (**www.arrl.org/triple-play**) is available to all amateurs worldwide who use Logbook of The World (LoTW) to confirm QSOs with each of the 50 states on voice, CW, and digital modes. All contacts *must* be confirmed in Logbook of The World — no QSL cards or other means of confirmation are eligible for this award.

Contacts must be made after 0000Z on January 1, 2009, to be considered for this award. LoTW automatically uses this criterion. There are no endorsements for the Triple Play WAS Award.

The Triple Play WAS Award is a serial-numbered award starting with #1, as determined by the time stamp of the electronic application submitted via LoTW. Awards issued are tracked and presented on the ARRL website.

Rules for Triple Play are similar to the other WAS awards. Two-way communications must be established on amateur bands with each state on each mode. There is no minimum signal report required. Any or all bands (except 60 meters) may be used for the Triple Play WAS. The District of Columbia may be counted for Maryland. Contacts must be made from the same location, or from locations no two of which are more than 50 miles apart. Club station applicants must include the club name and call sign of the club station (or trustee).

Contacts made through "repeater" devices or any other power relay method cannot be used for WAS confirmation. A separate WAS is available for Satellite contacts. All stations contacted must be "land stations." Contact with ships, anchored or otherwise, and aircraft, cannot be counted. EXCEPTION: Permanently docked exhibition ships, such as the Queen Mary and other historic ships will be considered land based.

A US applicant must be an ARRL member to participate in the WAS program. DX stations are exempt from this requirement.

Attempts to falsify data, logs, or other application operations may be grounds for disqualification. The decision of the ARRL Awards Committee in such cases is final.

Application instructions and fees for Triple Play WAS may be found on the LoTW website. In addition to a handsome certificate, plaques are available.

Worked All Continents (WAC)

In recognition of international two-way Amateur Radio communication, the International Amateur Radio Union (IARU) issues Worked All Continents (WAC) certificates to Amateur Radio stations around the world. WAC is issued for working and confirming two-way contacts with all six continents (North America, South America, Oceania, Asia, Europe, and Africa) on a variety of bands and modes. The ARRL DXCC List includes a continent designation for each DXCC country.

To apply for WAC, US amateurs must have current ARRL membership. All other applicants must be members of their national Amateur Radio Society affiliated with IARU and must apply through their Society only.

The following WAC certificates are available: Basic Certificate (mixed mode); CW Certificate; Phone Certificate; Image Certificate; Digital Certificate; Satellite Certificate.

The following WAC endorsements are available: QRP endorsement (5 W output or less); 1.8 MHz endorsement; 3.5 MHz endorsement; 50 MHz endorsement; 144 MHz endorsement; 430 MHz endorsement; 1270 MHz endorsement; any higher-band endorsement.

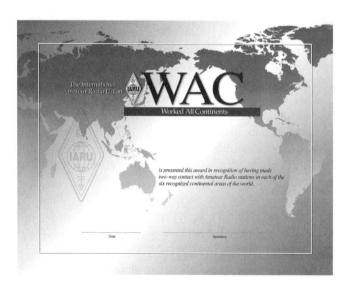

5 Band WAC: For the primary 5 Band WAC certificate, you must work six continents on each of these five bands: 10, 15, 20, 40, and 80 meters. Upon completion of these bands, endorsements are available for remaining amateur bands. A 6 Band WAC endorsement is available.

All contacts must be made from the same country or separate territory within the same continental area of the world. All QSL cards (no photocopies) must show the mode and/or band for any endorsement applied for.

Current rules and forms are available online at **www.iaru.org/wac/**. For amateurs in the US or countries without IARU representation, applications and QSL cards may be sent to the ARRL Awards Manager, 225 Main St, Newington, CT 06111. After verification, the cards will be returned, and the award sent soon afterward. Sufficient return postage for the cards is required.

For amateurs in the United States, QSL cards can also be approved by an official ARRL DXCC Card Checker (see **www.arrl.org/dxcc-card-checker-search**). QSOs listed in an applicant's DXCC award account in the DXCC computer system may also be used for confirmation. In this case, on the application form applicants MUST fill in details of the QSOs they want to use for WAC confirmation in the space provided.

QSO confirmations in ARRLs Logbook of The World (LoTW) system cannot be used for WAC confirmation.

Check **www.iaru.org/wac/** for the latest information about WAC and for the current fee schedule.

A-1 Operator Club (A-1 Op)

Only the best operators can qualify for membership in the A-1 Operator's Club. Members must demonstrate superior competence and performance in the many facets of Amateur Radio operation: CW, phone, procedures, copying ability, judgment, and courtesy. You must be recommended for the certification independently by two amateurs who are already A-1 Ops. This honor is unsolicited; it is earned through the continuous observance of the very highest operating standards. For more information, see **www.arrl.org/a-1-op**.

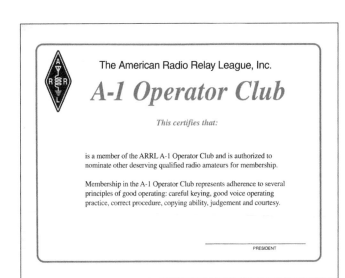

The American Radio Relay League, Inc.

A-1 Operator Club

This certifies that:

is a member of the ARRL A-1 Operator Club and is authorized to nominate other deserving qualified radio amateurs for membership.

Membership in the A-1 Operator Club represents adherence to several principles of good operating: careful keying, good voice operating practice, correct procedure, copying ability, judgement and courtesy.

PRESIDENT

Extra Class Certificate Program

Reminiscent of the *original* FCC Amateur Radio Extra Class License Certificate (no longer available), this beautiful certificate allows the Amateur Extra

licensee to display evidence of his achievement. The Amateur Extra Class Radio Operator certificate indicates the name and call sign of the operator as well as the date he or she achieved this top grade. Send your name (exactly as you wish it to appear) and address and the date you were issued your Amateur Extra license (the year is close enough) to the Awards Branch at ARRL HQ. Check **www.arrl.org/extra-class-program** for current processing fees for this certificate.

VHF/UHF Century Club Award

The VHF/UHF Century Club (VUCC) is awarded for contacts on 50 MHz and above with stations located in Maidenhead 2° × 1° grid locators. Grid locators are designated by a combination of two letters and two numbers (for example, W1AW is in FN31 in central Connecticut). More information on grid locators can be found in the VHF/UHF Operating chapter or online at **www.arrl.org/grid-squares**. The *ARRL Amateur Radio Map of North America*, *The ARRL World Grid Locator Atlas*, and the *ARRL Grid Locator for North America* are available from **www.arrl.org/shop** and show grid locators in the US.

The VUCC certificate and endorsements are available to amateurs worldwide. ARRL membership is required for US hams, possessions, and Puerto Rico. The minimum number of grid locators needed to qualify for a certificate is as follows: 50 MHz, 144 MHz and Satellite — 100 credits; 222 MHz and 432 MHz — 50 credits; 902 MHz and 1296 MHz — 25 credits; 2.3 GHz — 10 credits; 3.4 GHz, 5.7 GHz, 10 GHz,

24 GHz, 47 GHz, 75 GHz, 119 GHz, 142 GHz, 241 GHz and Laser (300 GHz) — 5 credits.

Endorsements are available for additional contacts at these levels: 50 MHz, 144 MHz and Satellite — 25; 222 MHz and 432 MHz — 10 credits; 902 MHz and above 5 credits

Contacts must be dated January 1, 1983, and later to count. Separate bands count for separate awards. Repeater and/or crossband contacts are not permitted except for Satellite awards. Contacts with aeronautical mobile stations do not count, but maritime mobiles are okay.

For VUCC awards on 50 through 1296 MHz and Satellite, all contacts must be made from locations no more than 200 km apart. For SHF awards, contacts must be made from a single location, defined as within a 300 meter diameter circle.

Application procedure (please follow carefully): Confirmations (QSLs) and application forms must be submitted to an approved VHF Awards Manager (Card Checker) for certification. You can download the most current rules and forms, as well as search for the nearest ARRL VHF Awards Manager, by following the links from **www.arrl.org/vucc**. If a VHF Awards Manager is not available, cards may be checked by an ARRL DXCC Card Checker (see **www.arrl.org/dxcc-card-checker-search**). Foreign VUCC applications should be checked by the Awards Manager for their IARU Member Society in their respective country. Do not send cards to HQ unless asked to do so.

For the convenience of the Awards Manager in checking cards, applicants may indicate in pencil (pencil *only*) the grid locator on the address side of the cards that do not clearly indicate the grid locator. The applicant affirms that he/she has accurately determined the proper location from the address information given on the card by signing the affirmation statement on the application. Cards must be sorted alphabetically by field and then numerically from 00 to 99 within that field. (For example, DM03, DM04, EN42, FN20, FM29, and so on.)

Where it is necessary to mail cards for certification, sufficient postage for proper return of all cards and paperwork, in addition to appropriate fees, must be included along with a separate self-addressed mailing label. An SASE is not necessary when a certificate will be issued, since a special mailing tube is used. ARRL accepts no responsibility for cards handled by mail to and from VHF Awards Managers and will not honor any claims.

Enclosed with the initial VUCC certificate from HQ will be a computer printout of the original list of grid locators for which the applicant has received credit. When applying for endorsements, the applicant will indicate in RED on the right hand side of the page those new grid locators for which credit is sought, and submit cards for certification to an Awards Manager. A new updated computer printout will be returned with appropriate endorsement sticker(s). Thus, a current list of grid locators worked is always in the hands of the VUCC award holder, available to the VHF Awards Manager during certification, and a permanent historical record always maintained at HQ.

VUCC awards are supported by Logbook of The World (LoTW). Instructions for setting up a VUCC account in LoTW and applying for awards may be found at **www.arrl.org/vucc**.

Fred Fish Memorial Award (FFMA)

The Fred Fish Memorial Award was created in honor of Fred Fish, W5FF (SK), who is the first amateur to have worked and confirmed all 488 Maidenhead grid squares in the 48 contiguous United States on 6 meters. The award will be given to any amateur who can duplicate W5FF's accomplishment. This award also encourages operation on the VHF bands from rare grid squares (known as Grid DXpeditions) to help activate all 488 grids.

The rules of FFMA closely follow the VUCC rules. Complete rules, application forms and resources such as a list of all required grid squares and a survey of rare grids may be found at **www.arrl.org/ffma**.

DX Century Club (DXCC)

DXCC is the premier operating award in Amateur Radio. The DXCC certificate is available to League members in the US and possessions, Puerto Rico, and all amateurs in the rest of the world. There are several DXCC awards available and fall roughly into four categories:

Mixed bands and modes: Mixed

Mode specific: Phone, CW, Digital, Satellite

Band specific: All contacts on 160, 80, 40, 30, 20, 17, 15, 12, 10, 6, or 2 meters and 70 cm.

The basic award level is 100 DXCC entities. Endorsements are available in specific increments beyond the 100 entity level. The DXCC Honor Roll is awarded to those participants who are closing

The American Radio Relay League, Inc.

DX CENTURY CLUB

This Certifies that

Has this day submitted evidence to the American Radio Relay League showing two-way communication with other amateur stations in at least one hundred different countries. This certificate recognizes outstanding performance and attests to membership in the DX Century Club.

President, ARRL

in on working all current entities, and the #1 Honor Roll plaque is available when you work them all.

The complete DXCC rules are quite lengthy. You can download the most current rules and forms, as well as search for the nearest DXCC Card Checker following the links from **www.arrl.org/dxcc**.

The DXCC Challenge

The DXCC Challenge Award is given for working and confirming at least 1000 DXCC Entities on any amateur bands, 1.8 through 54 MHz (except 60 meters). The Challenge award is in the form of a plaque, which can be endorsed in increments of 500. Entities for each band are totaled to give the Challenge standing. Deleted entities do not count for this award. All contacts must be made after November 15, 1945. QSOs for the 160, 80, 40, 30, 20, 17, 15, 12, 10, and 6 meter bands qualify for this award. Contacts on bands with fewer than 100 confirmed entities are acceptable for credit for this award. Check **www.arrl.org/dxcc** for fees and more information.

The DeSoto Cup is presented to the DXCC Challenge leader as of the 31st of December each year. The DeSoto Cup is named for Clinton B. DeSoto, whose definitive article in October 1935 *QST* forms the basis of the DXCC award. Only one cup will be awarded to any single individual. A medal will be presented to the winner in subsequent years. Medals will also be awarded to the second and third place winners each year.

5BDXCC

For those who enjoy the thrill of the hunt on more than one band, the Five-Band DXCC (5BDXCC) award is a formidable accomplishment. This award encourages more uniform DX activity throughout the amateur bands, encourages the development of more versatile antenna systems and equipment, provides a challenge for DXers, and enhances amateur-band occupancy.

The 5BDXCC certificate is issued after the applicant submits QSLs representing two-way contact with 100 different DXCC countries on each of the 80, 40, 20, 15, and 10 meter Amateur Radio bands. 5BDXCC is endorsable for additional bands: 160, 30, 17, 12, 6 and 2 meters. In addition to the 5BDXCC certificate, a 5BDXCC plaque is available at an extra charge.

ARRL DXCC List Criteria

The ARRL DXCC List is the result of progressive changes in DXing since 1945. Each entity on the ARRL DXCC List contains some definable political or geographical distinctiveness. While the general policy for qualifying entities for the ARRL DXCC List has remained the same, there has been considerable change in the specific details of criteria which are used to test entities for their qualifications. See the DXCC rules at **www.arrl.org/dxcc/** for the most current information.

QRP DXCC

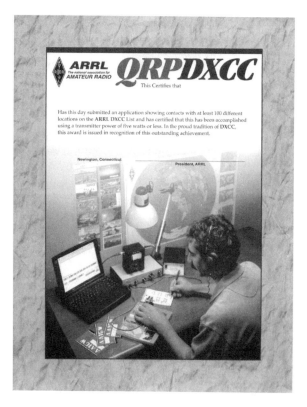

In recognition of the popularity of QRP (low power) operating, the ARRL offers the QRP DX Century Club, or QRP DXCC. The award is available to amateurs who have contacted at least 100 DXCC entities (see the list at **www.arrl. org/dxcc/**) using 5 W output or less, and standard DXCC rules apply. Contacts may have been made at any time since November 15, 1945, and no QSLs are required.

The QRP DXCC is a one-time award

and is non-endorsable. Certificates will be dated, but not numbered. This award is separate and distinct from the traditional DXCC award program. Credits are not assigned to other DXCC awards.

The award is available to amateurs worldwide, and you do not have to be an ARRL member to qualify. To apply for the QRP DXCC, just send a list of your contacts including call signs, countries/entities, and contact dates. Do not send QSLs. The list must also carry a signed statement from you that all of the contacts were made with 5 W RF output (as measured at the antenna system input) or less.

More information, forms, and the current application fee may be found at **www.arrl.org/qrp-dxcc**. Along with your contact list, include the application fee. Make sure to indicate your mailing address and your name as you want it to appear on the certificate. Mail everything to: QRP DXCC, ARRL, 225 Main St, Newington, CT 06111.

RSGB Islands On The Air — IOTA

The IOTA Program was created by Geoff Watts, a leading British shortwave listener, in the mid-1960s. When it was taken over by the RSGB in 1985 it had already become, for some, a favorite award. Its popularity grows each year and it is highly regarded among amateurs worldwide. The information given here is just a summary of the program. Full information, rules, and forms may be found at **www.rsgbiota.org**.

The IOTA Program consists of 21 separate certificates. They may be claimed by any licensed radio amateur eligible under the General Rules who can produce evidence of having made two-way communication since November 15, 1945, with the required number of Amateur Radio stations located on the islands both worldwide and regional. Part of the fun of IOTA is that it is an evolving program with new islands being activated for the first time.

The basic award is for working stations located on 100 islands/groups. There are higher achievement awards for working 200, 300, 400, 500, 600, 700, 800, 900, and 1000 islands/groups. In addition there are seven continental awards (including Antarctica) and three regional awards — Arctic Islands, British Isles and West Indies — for contacting a specified number of islands/groups listed in each area. The IOTA World Diploma is available for working 50% of the numbered groups in each of the seven continents. A Plaque of Excellence is available for confirmed contacts with at least 750 islands/groups. Shields are available for every 25 further islands/groups. The IOTA 1000 Islands Trophy is available for contacting 1000 IOTA groups. Mini plates are

available for additional IOTA groups in increments of 25.

Applicants must register and create an account on the IOTA website at **www.rsgbiota.org**. Electronic applications are strongly encouraged and award credits may be tracked online. The rules require that QSL cards be submitted to nominated IOTA checkpoints for checking. These checkpoints are listed on the IOTA website and in the *RSGB IOTA Directory and Yearbook*.

RSGB IOTA Directory

The official source of IOTA information is the *RSGB IOTA Directory*. This publication lists thousands of islands, grouped by continent and indexed by prefix, details the award rules, and provides application forms and a wealth of information and advice for the island enthusiast. The colorful new IOTA certificates are also shown. The latest *RSGB IOTA Directory* is an essential purchase for those interested in island-chasing. Copies are available from the ARRL at **www.arrl.org/shop**.

CQ Magazine Awards

Worked All Zones (WAZ)

The *CQ* WAZ Award will be issued to any licensed amateur station presenting proper QSL cards as proof of contact with the 40 zones of the world as defined in the award rules. QSL cards may be checked by any authorized *CQ* checkpoint or sent directly to the WAZ Award Manager, Floyd Gerald, N5FG, 17 Green Hollow Rd, Wiggins, MS 39577, e-mail

n5fg@cq-amateur-radio.com. Many of the major DX clubs in the United States and Canada and most national Amateur Radio societies abroad are authorized *CQ* checkpoints. Check the *CQ* website, **www.cq-amateur-radio.com**, for the current rules, zone lists, forms, checkpoints, processing fees, and payment information. Paper copies of zone maps, rules, and application forms are available from the WAZ Award Manager or CQ Communications, 25 Newbridge Rd, Hicksville, NY 11801. Send a business-size (4 × 9-inch), self-addressed envelope with two units of First-Class postage or $2 (US stations), or a self-addressed envelope and 3 IRCs (non-US stations).

The official *CQ* WAZ Zone Map and the printed zone list will be used to determine the zone in which a station is located. Confirmation must be accompanied by a list of claimed zones, using *CQ* Form 1479, showing the call letters of the station contacted within each zone. Form 1479 should also clearly show the applicant's name, call letters, and complete mailing address, as well as the award being applied for (such as Mixed, SSB, single band, and so forth).

All contacts must be made with licensed, land-based, amateur stations operating in authorized amateur bands, 160-10 meters. Any legal type of emission may be used, providing communication was established after November 15, 1945.

All contacts submitted by the applicant must be made from within the same country. It is recommended that each QSL clearly show the station's zone number. When the applicant submits cards for multiple call signs, evidence should be provided to show that he or she also held those call letters. Any altered or forged confirmations will result in permanent disqualification of the applicant. Decisions of the *CQ* DX Awards Advisory Committee on any matter pertaining to the administration of this award will be final.

All applications should be sent to the WAZ Award Manager after the QSL cards have been checked by an authorized *CQ* checkpoint.

WAZ By Mode and Band

In addition to the basic Mixed Mode award, certificates are available for these modes: AM, SSB, CW. RTTY, SSTV, and Digital (any digital mode except RTTY). (For these awards, all contacts must be two-way in that mode and so indicated on the QSL cards.)

WAZ awards are also issued for various bands: 160 Meters (mixed only, contacts starting January 1, 1975); 80, 40, 20, 15 or 10 meters (any single mode, contacts starting January 1, 1973); 30, 17 or 12 meters (any single mode, contacts starting January 1, 1991); Satellite (mixed only, contacts starting January 1, 1989); and 6 Meters and EME (mixed only, contacts starting January 1, 1973). Applications and cards for Digital, 160 Meters, Satellite, 6 Meters, and EME must be submitted directly to the WAZ Manager, not through checkpoints.

The 160 Meter WAZ Award requires that the applicant submit QSL cards from at least 30 zones. Stickers for 35, 36, 37, 38, 39, and 40 zones can be obtained from the WAZ Manager upon submission of the QSL cards and payment of the appropriate fees.

The Satellite and 6 Meter WAZ Awards require that the applicant submit QSL cards from at least 25 zones. Stickers for 30, 35, 36, 37, 38, 39, and 40 zones can be obtained from the WAZ Manager upon submission of the QSL cards and payment of the appropriate fees.

5 Band WAZ

CQ offers a most challenging DX award — 5 Band WAZ. Applicants who succeed in presenting proof of contact with the 40 zones of the world on these five HF bands — 80, 40, 20, 15 and 10 meters (for a total of 200) — will receive a special certificate in recognition of this achievement.

Contacts must be made after January 1, 1979, using any combination of modes (CW, SSB, RTTY). The award is available for Mixed Mode only. The first plateau, where the initial certificate is issued, requires a total of 150 of the possible 200 zones on a combination of the five bands. Applicants should use a separate sheet for each frequency band, using *CQ* Form 1479. Endorsements in increments of 10 are issued until the full 200 zone level is reached. A plaque is available at the 200 zone level.

Initial applications of up to 170 cards may be checked at an authorized checkpoint. Cards for all endorsements must be checked only by the WAZ Award Manager.

A regular WAZ or Single Band WAZ is a prerequisite for a 5 Band WAZ certificate. All applications should show the applicant's WAZ number. All applications should be sent to the WAZ Award Manager. The 5 Band WAZ Award is governed by the same rules as the regular WAZ Award and uses the same zone boundaries.

The CQ DX Awards Program

The *CQ* DX Award is issued in three categories: SSB, CW, and RTTY. Each award requires proof of contact with 100 or more countries using that mode. All QSOs must be 2× SSB, 2× CW or 2× RTTY. Cross-mode or one-way QSOs are not valid for the *CQ* DX Awards. All contacts must be with licensed land-based amateur stations working in authorized amateur bands. Contacts with ships and aircraft cannot be counted. QSLs must be listed in alphabetical order by prefix, and all QSOs must be dated after November 15, 1945. The application (Form 1067B) and full rules and current fees are available from the *CQ* website, **www.cq-amateur-radio.com**.

QSL cards must be verified by one of the authorized checkpoints for the *CQ* DX Awards or must be included with the application and sent to the Keith Gilbertson, KØKG, *CQ* DX Awards Manager, 21688 Sandy Beach Lane, Rochert, MN 56578. In all cases, include adequate funds for return postage.

Endorsement stickers are issued for 150, 200, 250, 275, 300, 310, and

320 countries. The ARRL DXCC List constitutes the basis for the *CQ* DX Award country status. Deleted countries will not be valid for the *CQ* DX Awards. If a DXCC country is deleted, it will automatically be deleted from *CQ* award records and totals readjusted accordingly. Special endorsement stickers are available for 3.5/7 MHz and 28 MHz (100 countries); 1.8 MHz, QRP, Mobile, SSTV, and Satellite (50 countries each).

The *CQ* DX Honor Roll lists all stations with a total of 275 countries or more. Separate Honor Rolls are maintained for SSB and CW. To remain on the Honor Roll, a station's country total must be updated annually.

CQ DX Field Award

The *CQ* DX Field Award rewards contacts with the 324 Maidenhead Grid Fields (10° latitude by 20° longitude rectangles lettered AA through RR). There are four categories — Mixed, CW, SSB, and Digital — and 50 confirmed QSOs are required for the initial award. Endorsements are available at various levels up to the full 324 Fields. Special endorsement stickers are available for various bands and modes. Check **www.cq-amateur-radio.com** for details and forms.

CQ WPX Award

The *CQ* WPX Award is for working different Amateur Radio prefixes around the world (NN1, DL7, JA6, 9J2, and so on). For portable stations, the portable designator becomes the prefix. For example, WN5N/7 counts as WN7 and J6/WN5N counts as J6.

Certificates are issued for contacts on HF (160-10 meters) and 6 meters. Awards start at 400 prefixes for Mixed Mode and 300 prefixes for single-mode awards —CW, SSB, and Digital. Cross-mode contacts are not eligible for single-mode awards. Endorsements are issued in increments of 50 prefixes.

Band endorsements are available for 1.8 MHz (50 prefixes), 3.5, and 5 MHz (175 prefixes), 7 and 10 MHz (250 prefixes) and 14 – 50 MHz (300 prefixes). Continent endorsements are available as well — North America (160 prefixes), South America (95 prefixes), Europe (160 prefixes), Africa (90 prefixes), Asia (75 prefixes), and Oceania (60 prefixes).

High scoring stations are eligible for the WPX Award of Excellence and for inclusion in the WPX Honor Roll.

As of mid-2012, *CQ* WPX Awards are supported by ARRL's Logbook of The World. LoTW users may track prefix confirmations and request credits toward *CQ* WPX awards. See **www.arrl.org/cq-awards** for details.

Applications (*CQ* form 1051) and appropriate fees should be sent to *CQ* WPX Award Manager Steve Bolia, N8BJQ, PO Box 355, New Carlisle,

OH 45344. Complete rules, forms and other resources are available at **www. cq-amateur-radio.com**.

County Hunting: USA-CA Program

The United States of America Counties Award (USA-CA), also sponsored by *CQ*, is issued for confirmed two-way radio contacts with specified numbers of US counties. Full rules, forms, and current fees are available from **www.cq-amateur-radio.com**.

The USA-CA is issued in seven different classes. Higher levels are awarded as endorsement seals for the basic certificate. Also, special endorsements will be made for all one band or mode operations subject to the rules.

Class	Counties Required	States Required
USA-500	500	Any
USA-1000	1000	25
USA-1500	1500	45
USA-2000	2000	50
USA-2500	2500	50
USA-3000	3000	50
USA 3077	ALL	50

USA-CA is available to all licensed amateurs everywhere in the world. You can accumulate contacts toward the USA-CA Award with any call sign you have held, and from any operating QTHs or dates. All contacts must be confirmed by QSL, and such QSLs must be in your possession for examination by USA-CA officials. QSL cards must not be altered in any way. QSOs via repeaters, satellites, moonbounce, and phone patches are not valid for USA-CA. So-called "team" contacts, where one person acknowledges a signal report and another returns a signal report, while both amateur call signs are logged, are not valid for USA-CA. Acceptable contact can be made with only one station at a time.

Unless otherwise indicated on QSL cards, the QTH printed on cards will determine county identity. For mobile and portable operations, the postmark shall identify the county unless other information is stated on QSL card to positively identify the county of operation. In the case of cities, parks or reservations not within counties proper, applicants may claim any one of adjoining counties for credit (once).

The USA-CA program is administered by a *CQ* staff member acting as USA-CA Custodian, and all applications and related correspondence should be sent directly to the custodian at his or her QTH. Decisions of the Custodian in administering these rules and their interpretation, including

future amendments, are final.

The scope of USA-CA makes it mandatory that special Record Books be used for application. For this purpose, *CQ* provides a 64-page 4.25 × 11-inch Record Book that contains application and certification forms and provides record-log space meeting the conditions of any class award and/or endorsement requested.

A completed USA-CA Record Book constitutes the medium of the basic award application and becomes the property of *CQ* for record purposes. On subsequent applications for either higher classes or for special endorsements, the applicant may use additional Record Books to list required data or may make up his own alphabetical list conforming to requirements. It is recommended that two be obtained, one for application use and one for personal file copy. See the USA-CA section of the *CQ* website for cost and ordering information.

Make Record Book entries necessary for county identity and enter other log data necessary to satisfy any special endorsements (band-mode) requested. Have the certification form provided signed by two licensed amateurs (General or higher) or an official of a national-level radio organization or affiliated club verifying the QSL cards for all contacts as listed have been seen.

The USA-CA custodian reserves the right to request any specific cards for any reason. In such cases, the applicant should send sufficient postage for return of cards by registered mail. Send the original completed Record Book (not a copy) and certification forms and handling fee to Ted Melinosky, K1BV, 12 Wells Woods Rd, Columbia, CT 06237. For later applications for higher-class seals, send the Record Book or self-prepared list per rules and handling fee. For application for later special endorsements (band/mode) where certificates must be returned for endorsement, send certificate and handling fee.

County hunter activity may be found daily on these frequencies: 14.336 MHz SSB, 14.066.5 MHz CW, and 10.122.5 MHz CW.

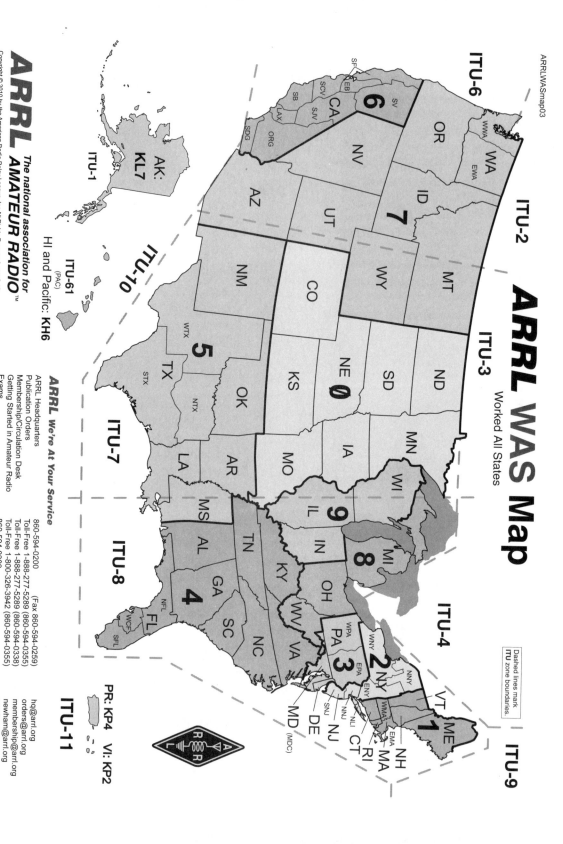

ARRLWASmap03

ARRL WAS Map

Worked All States

Dashed lines mark ITU zone boundaries.

ITU-6
ITU-2
ITU-3
ITU-4
ITU-9

AK: KL7
ITU-1

ITU-61
(PAC)

HI and Pacific: KH6

ITU-10

ITU-7

ITU-8

ITU-11

PR: KP4   VI: KP2

ARRL
The national association for
AMATEUR RADIO™

ARRL We're At Your Service

ARRL Headquarters   860-594-0200   (Fax: 860-594-0259)
Publication Orders   Toll-Free 1-888-277-5289 (860-594-0355)
Membership/Circulation Desk   Toll-Free 1-888-277-5289 (860-594-0338)
Getting Started in Amateur Radio   Toll-Free 1-800-326-3942 (860-594-0355)
Exams   860-594-0300
ARRL on the World Wide Web   www.arrl.org

hq@arrl.org
orders@arrl.org
membership@arrl.org
newham@arrl.org
vec@arrl.org

US Amateur Radio Bands

Published by:
ARRL The national association for **AMATEUR RADIO®**
www.arrl.org
225 Main Street, Newington, CT USA 06111-1494

Effective Date March 5, 2012

US AMATEUR POWER LIMITS

FCC 97.313 An amateur station must use the minimum transmitter power necessary to carry out the desired communications. (b) No station may transmit with a transmitter power exceeding 1.5 kW PEP.

160 Meters (1.8 MHz)
Avoid interference to radiolocation operations from 1.900 to 2.000 MHz

1.800 — 1.900 — 2.000 MHz   E,A,G

80 Meters (3.5 MHz)
3.500 3.525 3.600 3.600 3.700 3.800 4.000MHz
E / A / G / N,T (200 W)

60 Meters (5.3 MHz)
5330.5 5346.5 5357.0 5371.5 5403.5 kHz
2.8 kHz
E,A,G (100 W)

General, Advanced, and Amateur Extra licensees may operate on these five channels on a secondary basis with a maximum effective radiated output of 100 W PEP. Permitted operating modes include upper sideband voice (USB), CW, RTTY, PSK31 and other digital modes such as PACTOR III as defined by the FCC Report and Order of November 18, 2011. USB is limited to 2.8 kHz centered on 5332, 5348, 5358.5, 5373 and 5405 kHz. CW and digital emissions must be centered 1.5 kHz above the channel frequencies indicated above. Only one signal at a time is permitted on any channel.

40 Meters (7 MHz)
7.000 7.025 7.125 7.175 7.300 MHz
E / A / G / N,T (200 W)

Phone and Image modes are permitted between 7.075 and 7.100 MHz for FCC licensed stations in ITU Regions 1 and 3 and by FCC licensed stations in ITU Region 2 West of 130 degrees West longitude or South of 20 degrees North latitude. See Sections 97.305(c) and 97.307(f)(11). Novice and Technician licensees outside ITU Region 2 may use CW only between 7.025 and 7.075 MHz and between 7.100 and 7.125 MHz. 7.200 to 7.300 MHz is not available outside ITU Region 2. See Section 97.301(e). These exemptions do not apply to stations in the continental US.

30 Meters (10.1 MHz)
Avoid interference to fixed services outside the US.

10.100 — *200 Watts PEP* — 10.150 MHz   E,A,G

20 Meters (14 MHz)
14.000 14.025 14.150 14.175 14.225 14.350 MHz
E / A / G

17 Meters (18 MHz)
18.068 18.110 18.168 MHz   E,A,G

15 Meters (21 MHz)
21.000 21.025 21.200 21.225 21.275 21.450 MHz
E / A / G / N,T (200 W)

12 Meters (24 MHz)
24.890 24.930 24.990 MHz   E,A,G

10 Meters (28 MHz)
28.000 28.300 28.500 29.700 MHz
E,A,G / N,T (200 W)

6 Meters (50 MHz)
50.0 50.1 54.0 MHz   E,A,G,T

2 Meters (144 MHz)
144.0 144.1 148.0 MHz   E,A,G,T

1.25 Meters (222 MHz)
219.0 220.0 222.0 225.0 MHz
E,A,G,T / N (25 W)

70 cm (420 MHz) *
420.0 450.0 MHz   E,A,G,T

33 cm (902 MHz) *
902.0 928.0 MHz   E,A,G,T

23 cm (1240 MHz) *
1240 1270 1295 1300 MHz
E,A,G,T / N (5 W)

* No pulse emissions

*Geographical and power restrictions may apply to all bands above 420 MHz. See *The ARRL Operating Manual* for information about your area.

All licensees except Novices are authorized all modes on the following frequencies:
2300-2310 MHz   10.0-10.5 GHz *
2390-2450 MHz   24.0-24.25 GHz
3300-3500 MHz   47.0-47.2 GHz
5650-5925 MHz   76.0-81.0 GHz

122.25-123.0 GHz
134-141 GHz
241-250 GHz
All above 275 GHz

KEY

Note:
CW operation is permitted throughout all amateur bands.
MCW is authorized above 50.1 MHz, except for 144.0-144.1 and 219-220 MHz.
Test transmissions are authorized above 51 MHz, except for 219-220 MHz

See *ARRLWeb* at www.arrl.org for detailed band plans.

ARRL — We're At Your Service
ARRL Headquarters:
860-594-0200 (Fax 860-594-0259)
email: hq@arrl.org

Publication Orders:
www.arrl.org/shop
Toll-Free 1-888-277-5289 (860-594-0355)
email: orders@arrl.org

Membership/Circulation Desk:
www.arrl.org/membership
Toll-Free 1-888-277-5289 (860-594-0338)
email: membership@arrl.org

Getting Started in Amateur Radio:
Toll-Free 1-800-326-3942 (860-594-0355)
email: newham@arrl.org

Exams: 860-594-0300 email: vec@arrl.org

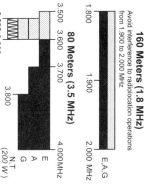
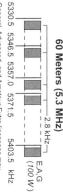
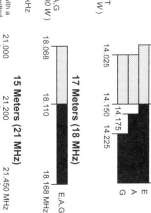

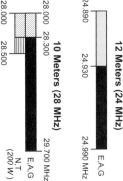
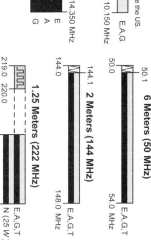

CW Abbreviations

AA	All after	HI	The telegraphic laugh; high	SKED	Schedule
AB	All before	HR	Here, hear	SRI	Sorry
AB	About	HV	Have	SSB	Single sideband
ADR	Address	HW	How	SVC	Service; prefix to service message
AGN	Again	LID	A poor operator		
ANT	Antenna	MA, MILS	Milliamperes	T	Zero
BCI	Broadcast interference	MSG	Message; prefix to radiogram	TFC	Traffic
BCL	Broadcast listener	N	No	TMW	Tomorrow
BK	Break; break me; break in	NCS	Net control station	TNX-TKS	Thanks
BN	All between; been	ND	Nothing doing	TT	That
BUG	Semi-automatic key	NIL	Nothing; I have nothing for you	TU	Thank you
B4	Before	NM	No more	TVI	Television interference
C	Yes	NR	Number	TX	Transmitter
CFM	Confirm; I confirm	NW	Now; I resume transmission	TXT	Text
CK	Check	OB	Old boy	UR-URS	Your; you're; yours
CL	I am closing my station; call	OC	Old chap	VFO	Variable-frequency oscillator
CLD-CLG	Called; calling	OM	Old man	VY	Very
CQ	Calling any station	OP-OPR	Operator	WA	Word after
CUD	Could	OT	Old timer; old top	WB	Word before
CUL	See you later	PBL	Preamble	WD-WDS	Word; words
CW	Continuous wave (i.e., radio-telegraph)	PSE	Please	WKD-WKG	Worked; working
		PWR	Power	WL	Well; will
DE	From	PX	Press	WUD	Would
DLD-DLVD	Delivered	R	Received as transmitted; are	WX	Weather
DR	Dear	RCD	Received	XCVR	Transceiver
DX	Distance, foreign countries	RCVR (RX)	Receiver	XMTR (TX)	Transmitter
ES	And, &	REF	Refer to; referring to; reference	XTAL	Crystal
FB	Fine business, excellent	RFI	Radio Frequency Interference	XYL (YF)	Wife
FM	Frequency modulation	RIG	Station equipment	YL	Young lady
GA	Go ahead (or resume sending)	RPT	Repeat; I repeat; report	73	Best regards
GB	Good-by	RTTY	Radioteletype	88	Love and Kisses
GBA	Give better address	RX	Receiver		
GE	Good evening	SASE	Self-addressed, stamped envelope		
GG	Going				
GM	Good morning	SED	Said		
GN	Good night	SIG	Signature; signal		
GND	Ground	SINE	Operator's personal initials or nickname		
GUD	Good				

Although abbreviations help to cut down unnecessary transmission, make it a rule not to abbreviate unnecessarily when working an operator of unknown experience.

ITU Recommended Phonetics

A — Alfa (**AL** FAH)
B — Bravo (**BRAH** VOH)
C — Charlie (**CHAR** LEE OR **SHAR** LEE)
D — Delta (**DELL** TAH)
E — Echo (**ECK** OH)
F — Foxtrot (**FOKS** TROT)
G — Golf (GOLF)
H — Hotel (HOH **TELL**)
I — India (**IN** DEE AH)
J — Juliet (**JEW** LEE ETT)
K — Kilo (**KEY** LOH)
L — Lima (**LEE** MAH)
M — Mike (MIKE)
N — November (NO **VEM** BER)
O — Oscar (**OSS** CAH)
P — Papa (PAH **PAH**)

Q — Quebec (KEH **BECK**)
R — Romeo (**ROW** ME OH)
S — Sierra (SEE *AIR* RAH)
T — Tango (**TANG** GO)
U — Uniform (**YOU** NEE FORM or **OO** NEE FORM)
V — Victor (**VIK** TAH)
W — Whiskey (**WISS** KEY)
X — X-Ray (**ECKS** RAY)
Y — Yankee (**YANG** KEY)
Z — Zulu (**ZOO** LOO)

Note: The **Boldfaced** syllables are emphasized. The pronunciations shown in the table were designed for speakers from all international languages. The pronunciations given for "Oscar" and "Victor" may seem awkward to English-speaking people in the U.S.

ARRL Procedural Signals (Prosigns)

In general, the CW prosigns are used on all data modes as well, although word abbreviations may be spelled out. That is, "CLEAR" might be used rather than "CL" on radioteletype. Additional radioteletype conventions appear at the end of the table.

Situation	CW	Voice
check for a clear frequency	QRL?	Is the frequency in use?
seek contact with any station	CQ	CQ
after call to specific named station or to indicate end of message	AR	over, end of message
invite any station to transmit	K	go
invite a specific named station to transmit	KN	go only
invite receiving station to transmit	BK	back to you
all received correctly	R	received
please stand by	AS	wait, stand by
end of contact (sent before call sign)	SK	clear
going off the air	CL	closing station

Additional RTTY prosigns

SK QRZ—Ending contact, but listening on frequency.
SK KN—Ending contact, but listening for one last transmission from the other station.
SK SZ—Signing off and listening on the frequency for any other calls.

Q Signals

These Q signals most often need to be expressed with brevity and clarity in amateur work. (Q abbreviations take the form of questions only when each is sent followed by a question mark.)

QRA   What is the name of your station? The name of your station is _____.

QRG   Will you tell me my exact frequency (or that of _____)? Your exact frequency (or that of _____) is _____ kHz.

QRH   Does my frequency vary? Your frequency varies.

QRI   How is the tone of my transmission? The tone of your transmission is _____ (1. Good; 2. Variable; 3. Bad).

QRJ   Are you receiving me badly? I cannot receive you. Your signals are too weak.

QRK   What is the intelligibility of my signals (or those of _____)? The intelligibility of your signals (or those of _____) is _____ (1. Bad; 2. Poor; 3. Fair; 4. Good; 5. Excellent).

QRL   Are you busy? I am busy (or I am busy with _____). Please do not interfere.

QRM   Is my transmission being interfered with? Your transmission is being interfered with (1. Nil; 2. Slightly; 3. Moderately; 4. Severely; 5. Extremely.)

QRN   Are you troubled by static? I am troubled by static _____ (1-5 as under QRM).

QRO   Shall I increase power? Increase power.

QRP   Shall I decrease power? Decrease power.

QRQ   Shall I send faster? Send faster (_____ WPM).

QRS   Shall I send more slowly? Send more slowly (_____ WPM).

QRT   Shall I stop sending? Stop sending.

QRU   Have you anything for me? I have nothing for you.

QRV   Are you ready? I am ready.

QRW   Shall I inform _____ that you are calling on _____ kHz? Please inform _____ that I am calling on _____ kHz.

QRX   When will you call me again? I will call you again at _____ hours (on _____ kHz).

QRY   What is my turn? Your turn is numbered _____

QRZ   Who is calling me? You are being called by _____ (on _____ kHz).

QSA   What is the strength of my signals (or those of _____)? The strength of your signals (or those of _____) is _____

(1. Scarcely perceptible; 2. Weak; 3. Fairly good; 4. Good; 5. Very good).

QSB   Are my signals fading? Your signals are fading.

QSD   Is my keying defective? Your keying is defective.

QSG   Shall I send _____ messages at a time? Send _____ messages at a time.

QSK   Can you hear me between your signals and if so can I break in on your transmission? I can hear you between my signals; break in on my transmission.

QSL   Can you acknowledge receipt? I am acknowledging receipt.

QSM   Shall I repeat the last message which I sent you, or some previous message? Repeat the last message which you sent me [or message(s) number(s) _____].

QSN   Did you hear me (or _____) on _____ kHz? I did hear you (or _____) on _____ kHz.

QSO   Can you communicate with _____ direct or by relay? I can communicate with _____ direct (or by relay through _____).

QSP   Will you relay to _____? I will relay to _____

QST   General call preceding a message addressed to all amateurs and ARRL members. This is in effect "CQ ARRL."

QSU   Shall I send or reply on this frequency (or on _____ kHz)? Send or reply on this frequency (or _____ kHz).

QSV   Shall I send a series of Vs on this frequency (or on _____ kHz)? Send a series of Vs on this frequency (or on _____ kHz).

QSW   Will you send on this frequency (or on _____ kHz)? I am going to send on this frequency (or on _____ kHz).

QSX   Will you listen to _____ on _____ kHz? I am listening to _____ on _____ kHz.

QSY   Shall I change to transmission on another frequency? Change to transmission on another frequency (or on _____ kHz).

QSZ   Shall I send each word or group more than once? Send each word or group twice (or _____ times).

QTA   Shall I cancel message number _____? Cancel message number _____

QTB   Do you agree with my counting of words? I do not agree

	with your counting of words. I will repeat the first letter or digit of each word or group.
QTC	How many messages have you to send? I have _____ messages for you (or for _____).
QTH	What is your location? My location is _____
QTR	What is the correct time? The correct time is _____
QTV	Shall I stand guard for you? Stand guard for me.
QTX	Will you keep your station open for further communication with me? Keep your station open for me.
QUA	Have you news of _____? I have news of _____.

ARRL QN Signals

QNA*	Answer in prearranged order.
QNB	Act as relay between _____ and _____.
QNC	All net stations copy. I have a message for all net stations.
QND*	Net is Directed (Controlled by net control station.)
QNE*	Entire net stand by.
QNF	Net is Free (not controlled).
QNG	Take over as net control station
QNH	Your net frequency is High.
QNI	Net stations report in. I am reporting into the net. (Follow with a list of traffic or QRU.)
QNJ	Can you copy me?
QNK*	Transmit messages for _____ to _____.
QNL	Your net frequency is Low.
QNM*	You are QRMing the net. Stand by.
QNN	Net control station is _____. What station has net control?
QNO	Station is leaving the net.
QNP	Unable to copy you. Unable to copy _____.

QNQ*	Move frequency to _____ and wait for _____ to finish handling traffic. Then send him traffic for _____.
QNR*	Answer _____ and Receive traffic.
QNS	Following Stations are in the net.* (follow with list.) Request list of stations in the net.
QNT	I request permission to leave the net for _____ minutes.
QNU*	The net has traffic for *you*. Stand by.
QNV*	Establish contact with _____ on this frequency. If successful, move to _____ and send him traffic for _____.
QNW	How do I route messages for _____?
QNX	You are excused from the net.*
QNY*	Shift to another frequency (or to _____ kHz) to clear traffic with _____.
QNZ	Zero beat your signal with mine.

*For use only by the Net Control Station.

Notes on Use of QN Signals

These QN signals are special ARRL signals for use in amateur CW nets *only*. They are not for use in casual amateur conversation. Other meanings that may be used in other services do not apply. Do not use QN signals on phone nets. *Say it with words*. QN signals need not be followed by a question mark, even though the meaning may be interrogatory.

The RST System

Readability

1—Unreadable.
2—Barely readable, occasional words distinguishable.
3—Readable with considerable difficulty.
4—Readable with practically no difficulty.
5—Perfectly readable.

Signal Strength

1—Faint signals, barely perceptible.
2—Very weak signals.
3—Weak signals.
4—Fair signals.
5—Fairly good signals.
6—Good signals.
7—Moderately strong signals.
8—Strong signals.
9—Extremely strong signals.

Tone

1—Sixty-cycle ac or less, very rough and broad.
2—Very rough ac, very harsh and broad.
3—Rough ac tone, rectified but not filtered.
4—Rough note, some trace of filtering.
5—Filtered rectified ac but strongly ripple-modulated.
6—Filtered tone, definite trace of ripple modulation.
7—Near pure tone, trace of ripple modulation.
8—Near perfect tone, slight trace of modulation.
9—Perfect tone, no trace of ripple of modulation of any kind.
If the signal has the characteristic steadiness of crystal control, add the letter X to the RST report. If there is a chirp, add the letter C. Similarly for a click, add letter K. (See FCC Regulations §97.307, Emissions Standards.) The above reporting system is used on both CW and voice; leave out the "tone" report on voice.

Logbook of the World in 6 Steps

Step 1

Download Trusted QSL Software

Logbook of The World uses a software package called Trusted QSL. The Trusted QSL software that you downloaded and installed on your computer Is where you will manage all LoTW functions including call sign certificates, station locations and signing and uploading your log files.

Trusted QSL software is available for Windows and Mac OSX operating systems.

Linux users can build the software from the source code for the tqsllib library and the TrustedQSL applications. (ARRL does not maintain packages for the plethora of Linux distributions. For assistance with obtaining a packaged version for your Linux distribution, contact your distribution's maintainer.)

The software is downloaded from the web at www.arrl.org/instructions

1. From the web page http://www.arrl.org/instructions click the link to begin downloading the software for your operating system, PC or MAC.

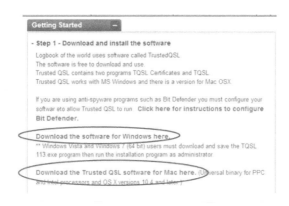

Choose TQSL either for Window or TQSL for Mac.

Trusted QSL uses a Windows installer

Just click NEXT and agree to the terms then install.

When the program is finished installing you will have an icon on your desktop that looks like this:

Double clicking this icon will open the Trusted QSL program. Proceed to the next step.

Step 2

Requesting Your Certificate

Logbook of The World uses private key – public key encryption. The Trusted QSL software that you downloaded and installed on your computer contains two programs – Trusted QSL (TQSL) and Trusted QSL Certificates (TQSL CERT). All certificates are managed in the TQSL CERT program.

A certificate request (TQ5 file) is sent to ARRL and is answered with a TQ6 file. When the TQ6 file is loaded into TQSL CERT you will have your certificate, as indicated by the gold ribbon next to your call sign, which you will use to electronically sign your log files.

The TQ5 and TQ6 files contain unique digital signatures and must match each other like two halves of a torn ticket. Any previous certificate request is nullified when a new request is made so do not delete or alter any files after making a certificate request.

Because the request and response must match the entire process must be completed from the same computer. Once you have a complete certificate moving it to a new or second computer is only matter of a few clicks with your mouse. (See www.arrl.org/instructions Secondary Operations, Moving To a New or Second Computer.)

Requesting a certificate is not difficult. It is simply a matter of entering some basic information about you and your call sign then saving a file – TQ5 and sending the file to LoTW.

In this procedure we are going to request a certificate for your current call sign.

The procedure below will guide you through each screen of the process. Let's begin.

After you have installed the Trusted QSL software you will have a program icon on your desktop.

1. Open the **TQSL** program by double clicking the icon on your desktop.

When opening the **TQSL** for the first time you will get an alert stating that you have no certificates and asks if you would like to request a certificate.

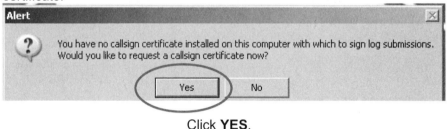

Click **YES**.

- If you inadvertently answered NO to the above question Select Call sign Certificate tab then select Request New Call sign certificate…

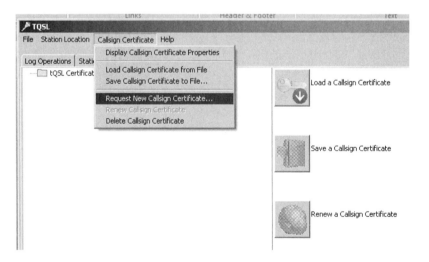

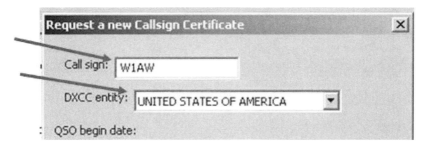

2. Enter your **CURRENT CALL SIGN** without any portable identifiers. This is your primary call sign. Later you will be able to request certificates for additional or secondary call signs such as old calls or portable calls.

3. Use the drop down menu to select the DXCC entity that matches your call and where you are operating.

   If you hold a **KH6 or KL7** call sign and
   - Your FCC address is Hawaii or Alaska then your DXCC entity will be Hawaii or Alaska.
   - Your FCC address is in the continental United States then your DXCC entity will be United States of America.

DL stations:

Your DXCC entity is **Federal Republic of Germany (FRG).**

From DXCC Deleted Countries notes.

[18] (DA-DM) Only contacts made September 16, 1973, and before, count for this entity. Contacts made September 17, 1973, and after, count as either FRG (DA-DL) or GDR(Y2-Y9).

[19] (DM, Y2-Y9) Only contacts made from September 17, 1973 and October 2, 1990 count for this entity. On October 3, 1990 the GDR became part of the FRG.

For DXCC prior to Sept 17, 1973 West Germany was GERMANY

If you operated form any of the German nations prior to September 17, 1973 this is what you will have to do:

1. First you will get your primary UNSIGNED certificate DL#xxx starting September 17, 1973 and the country will be Federal Republic of Germany.

2. After the certificate is process and you have the gold ribbon in TQSL CERT Next you will request a SIGNED certificate from the date you received the call sign (after November 11,1945) until Sept 16, 1973 for DL#xxx and the country will be GERMANY.

3. Ops from the former East Germany will have to get a third certificate to cover the time from Sept 17, 1973 until October 2, 1990 when they were **German Democratic Republic (GDR)**

The QSO Date Range will determine which QSOs in your log can be uploaded to Logbook of The World.

It is important that you enter correct information. The QSO date range cannot be changed once the certificate is issued.

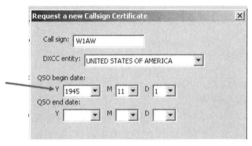

4. QSO **BEGIN** date should be the date that this call sign was first issued to you. If you are unsure of this date then use the earliest date in your log for QSOs using this call sign.
   - Do not use today's date.
   - This may not necessarily be the date you were first licensed if you held another call prior to your current call sign.
   - Do not use your birthday or any other date.

Currently active calls will not have a QSO END DATE. Entering a QSO END DATE for a current call will limit the QSOs that can be uploaded for this call.

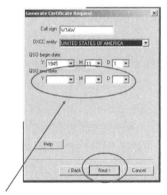

Leave blank for currently active call signs.

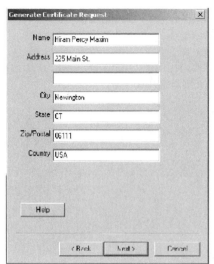 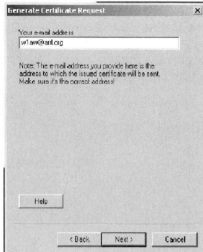

5. Enter your name and address. For U.S licensees this must match your FCC address. Click **NEXT.**

6. Enter your e-mail address.

   - Make sure that your e-mail provider allows attachments. You will receive your TQ6 certificate file, username and website password in an e-mail.

This next step is optional.

A password is recommended if you use a public computer or run LoTW/TQSL with a portable computer.

If you choose to use a private key password please write it down so you do not forget it.

If you lose or forget this password ARRL cannot help you.

To fix a lost private key password, you will need to apply for a new certificate.

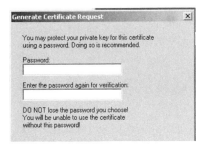

7. Enter a password if you choose this option.
   - You may leave this blank for no password. (Recommended)
   - Remember that if you lose or forget this password we cannot help you.

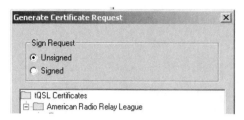

8. Be sure that your request is **UNSIGNED**.
   - Because this is your first certificate request your only choice should be **UNSIGNED**.

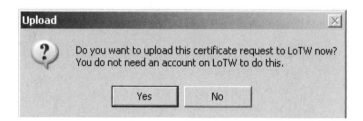

9. You will be asked if you want to send this request to LoTW. If you have an internet connection then click **YES** and the request will be uploaded to the LoTW server.

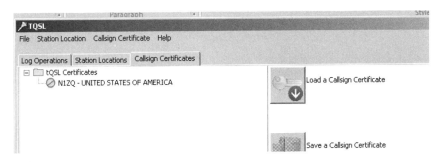

When done correctly your TQSL CERT window should look like this with a slashed red circle "Do Not Enter" sign, your call sign and your DXCC entity.

It is important that you do not delete or move or rename any files or folders. Do not delete the red slashed circle.

Option to e-mail the certificate request file (TQ5)

If you answered **NO** to the above question you will have saved a TQ5 file to your folders. You may send that file as an attachment to an e-mail to Lotw-logs@arrl.org

Do not attach anything else to this e-mail or include any message. This e-mail is sent to a robot that only looks to TrustedQSL files.

* If you are submitting a cert request for a **non-US call sign**, you will have to submit proof of license (a copy) and a copy of one other official document that shows your name, like a driver's license. See https://www.arrl.org/lotw/docreq for details.

Postcards and documents are used only during the initial account set up and are not required for once you have established your LoTW account.

Step 3

Enter your Postcard Password

Note! This applies only to USA licensees!

1. Go to the Postcard Password Entry webpage:
   https://p1k.arrl.org/lotw/password

2. Enter your callsign in the callsign box and enter the password exactly as it is on the card in the password box.   The password is eight alpha-numeric characters above the address and batch numbers on the front of your postcard. The password is case sensitive.

3. Click SUBMIT PASSWORD

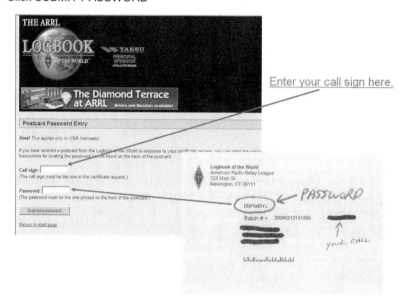

4. Your certificate request has now been verified. You will receive your certificate (TQ6 file) as an e-mail attachment within three business days.
   This e-mail will also contain your password to log onto the LoTW users page and access your account. Your Log-on ID is your callsign. You can/should change this password after you log-on.

Accepting an Initial Callsign Certificate

LoTW requires that you accept your Initial Callsign Certificate using the same computer from which you generated the request for your Initial Callsign Certificate.

These instructions assume that your Callsign Certificate reside in the folder C:\MyLoTWCertificates (if you've stored them in a different folder, adjust the instructions accordingly).

When you receive an email message from the ARRL with an attached file named YourCallsign.tq6 (for example, CT2IRY.tq6),

1. Direct your email application to open the email message.

1.a The attached file contains your Initial Callsign Certificate -- save it into the folder C:\MyLotWCertificates

1.b The e-mail message will contain a Web Account Username and a Web Account Password; be sure to record these, as they are required to view your uploaded QSOs and LoTW-generated confirmations via https://p1k.arrl.org/lotwuser/default

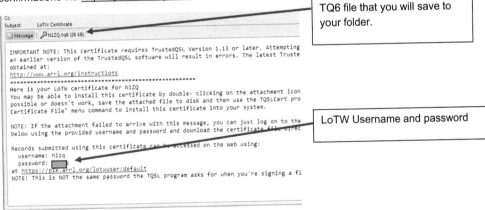

TQ6 file that you will save to your folder.

LoTW Username and password

2. To proceed, the YourCallsign.tq5 file must be present in C:\MyLotW\Certificates ; if you deleted this file, or initiated the request from a different computer, you'll have to start over by requesting a new Callsign Certificate from the ARRL.

3. Start TQSL and select the Callsign Certificates tab:

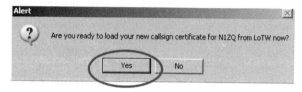

3.a When opening TQSL you may be asked if you want to load a certificate. Answer YES and proceed to 3.b.2

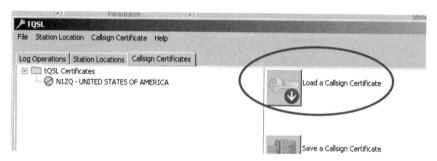

3.b Click the Load a Callsign Certificate button; the Select Certificate File dialog will appear

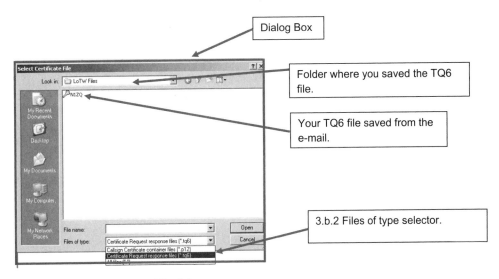

Dialog Box

Folder where you saved the TQ6 file.

Your TQ6 file saved from the e-mail.

3.b.2 Files of type selector.

3.b.1 In the Select Certificate File dialog,

3.b.2 Set the Files of type selector (on OS X, set the Enable selector) to Certificate Request response files (*.tq6)

3.b.2. Select the file YourCallsign.tq6 in your C:\MyLotWCertificates folder

3.b.3. Click the Open button; a small Install Certificate dialog will appear.

3.c In the Install Certificate dialog, you'll be asked if its okay to install a trusted root certificate; click the Yes button

3.d In the Load Certificate File dialog, click the Finish button.

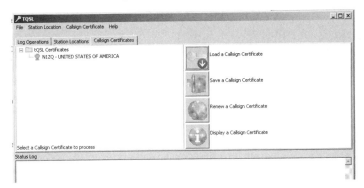

3.e The Callsign Certificates tab will show an entry for your Callsign Certificate, with a yellow medal valid icon.

Step 5

Defining or Modifying a Station Location

A *Station Location* specifies both a <u>Callsign Certificate</u> and an operating location.

Defining a Station Location

1. In TQSL, select the **Station Locations** tab and click the **Create a new Station Location** button; the **Add Station Location** dialog will appear.

2. In the **Add Station Location** dialog, specify your callsign, grid square, ITU zone, CQ zone, and IOTA Reference Number.

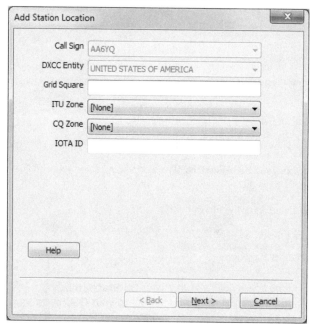

2.a select your callsign

2.b specify the **Grid Square** in which your station is located (this is particularly important if you operate on VHF or UHF frequencies or via Satellites, as it provides Grid Square credit to your QSO partners pursuing VUCC awards)

2.c specify the **ITU Zone** in which your station is located

2.d specify the **CQ Zone** in which your station is located

2.e if your station is located on an island, specify its **IOTA Reference Number**; use a two-character continent abbreviation followed by a dash and a 3 digit number, e.g. OC-005. If you do not know your IOTA designation, you can find this information at http://www.rsgbiota.org

2.f click the **Next** button

> **Note**: if the **DXCC Entity**, **ITU Zone**, and **CQ Zone** are mutually inconsistent, an ***Invalid zone selections for DXCC entity*** message will be displayed, and the **Next** button will be disabled; you must select consistent **ITU** and **CQ** zones before proceeding.

3. Depending upon your callsign's DXCC entity, the **Add Station Location** dialog may prompt you to specify your Province, Oblast, State, and/or County. The example below shows this for a station in the United States:

3.a in the **Add Station Location** dialog, select your US **State** (this is particularly important as it provides US State credit to your QSO partners pursuing WAS awards)

3.b select your US **County**

3.c click the **Next** button

4. in the **Add Station Location** dialog, specify a **Station Location Name.**

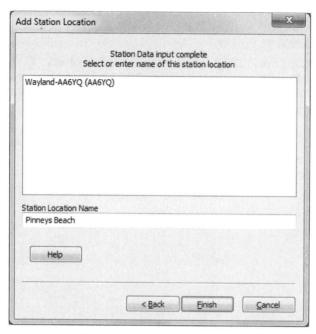

4.a to make this name meaningful, it is recommended that it incorporate both your callsign and town name, or callsign and location name (see Additional Information below)

4.b click the **Finish** button

4.c to protect your new Station Location, direct TQSL to create a Backup File.

Modifying a Station Location

1. In TQSL, select the **Station Locations** tab, which lists your Station Locations:

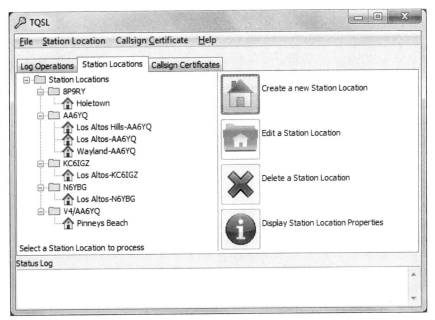

2. On the **Stations Locations** tab, click on the name of the Station Location you wish modify:

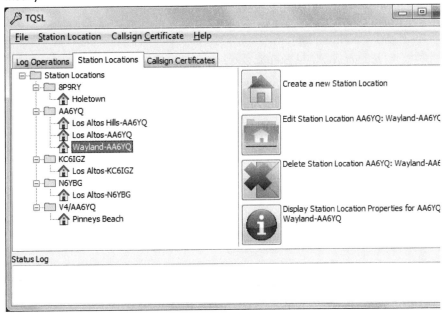

and then click the **Edit Station Location** button; the **Edit Station Location** dialog appear.

3. In the **Edit Station Location** dialog, select a different callsign, or modify the grid square, ITU zone, CQ zone, or IOTA tag as desired.

4. Click the **Next** button. Note: if the **DXCC Entity**, **ITU Zone**, and **CQ Zone** are mutu inconsistent, an ***Invalid zone selections for DXCC entity*** message will be display and the **Next** button will be disabled; you must select consistent **ITU** and **CQ** zones before proceeding.

5. If your station is in a DXCC entity for which a Province, Oblast, State, and/or County be selected, modify your selection(s) as desired.

6. Click the **Next** button.

7. Modify the Station Location Name as desired.

8. Click the **Finish** button.

9. To protect your modified Station Location, direct TQSL to create a <u>Backup File</u>.

Additional Information

- If you always operate with the same callsign and from one location, use a name that combines them both, e.g. K9UW(Amherst) or AA5AU-Louisiana. If you operate with more than one callsign or from more than one location, see this <u>example</u>.

- You can <u>move a Station Location from one computer to another</u>

Submitting a Log File to LoTW via the Internet

To digitally sign a log file and upload via the Internet to the ARRL's Logbook of the World (LoTW) online service,

1. Verify that all of the QSOs in the log file were made with the same *Station Callsign* (the callsign you used over the air during the QSO), and from the same location. If this isn't the case, use your logging application or a text editor to split the log file into multiple log files, each of whose QSOs were made with the same Station Callsign from the same operating location, and separately submit each log file.

2. Start **TQSL**. If you do this before receiving your **Initial Callsign Certificate**, an **Alert** window will appear that informs you that you have no Certificate, and asks if you want to request one; click the **Yes** button, and proceed as described here.

3. Select the **Log Operations** tab

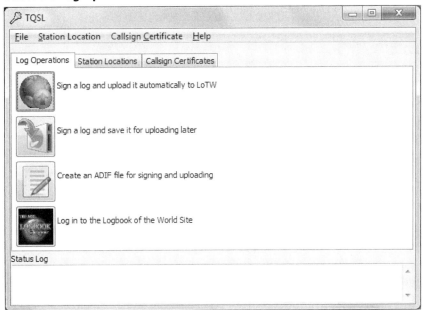

   and click the **Sign a log and upload it automatically to LoTW** button.

4. In the **Select File to Sign** dialog,

   4.a Set the **Files of type** selector (on **OS X**, set the **Enable** selector) to *ADIF files* or *Cabrillo files*.

      * You can digitally sign Cabrillo log files for these contests without additional configuration.

* When submitting a Cabrillo log file, mode PH is submitted as SSB

* If your logging application does not ensure that only new or newly modified QSOs are presented to TQSL for submission to LoTW, enabling the Prompt for QSO Date Range option will help spare LoTW from having to process QSOs that it's already processed.

* You can change the file extensions displayed when you set the **Files of type** selector.

* You can enable or disable the submission of nonamateur callsigns.

4.b Navigate to the folder containing the log file you wish to submit

4.c Select log file you wish to submit

4.d Click the **Open** button

5. In the **Select Station Location for Signing** dialog, select the Station Location that specifies the Callsign and operating location used to make the log file's QSOs, and click the **Ok** button.

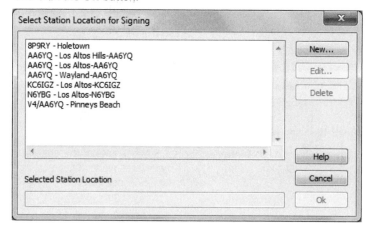

6. In the **TQSL - Confirm signing** dialog, verify that the information displayed is correct, and click the **Yes** button.

7. If TQSL is configured to not submit QSOs that lie outside a specified date range, the QSO Date Range dialog will appear; specify the desired **Start Date** and **End Date**, and click the **Ok** button.

If your logging application does not ensure that only new or newly modified QSOs are presented to TQSL for submission to LoTW, the QSO Date Range dialog can help prevent the submission of QSOs that have already been uploaded and processed.

8. If the Callsign Certificate associated with the selected Station Location is password-protected, the **Enter password** dialog will appear; enter the password, and click the **OK** button.

9. If TQSL detects any QSOs in the log file that have already been submitted to LoTW and haven't been subsequently modified, it will display the **Duplicate QSOs Detected** dialog:

9.a Click the **Exclude duplicates** button to continue processing, ignoring the duplicate QSOs (recommended)

9.b Click the **Cancel** button to abandon processing so you can either select a log file that doesn't contain duplicate QSOs, or use the QSO Date Range dialog to exclude duplicate QSOs

9.c Click the **Allow Duplicates** button to submit the duplicate QSOs; note that the digitally signed log file submitted to LoTW will be marked as containing duplicate QSOs

Note: if all QSOs in the log file are duplicates, the **Exclude duplicates** button will not be displayed

10. The **Status Log** in TQSL's main window will display the results of the operation, including the number of QSOs ignored because their dates were outside of the specified Date Range, and the number of duplicate QSOs detected:

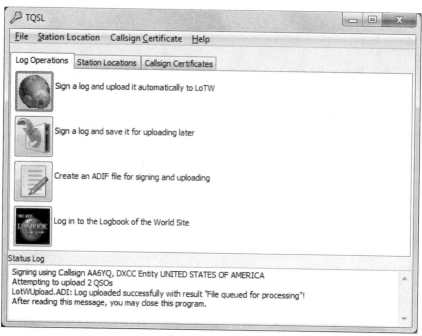

10.a If the upload to LoTW failed, a dialog box will be displayed offering to repeat the upload; click **Yes** to upload the digitally signed file again, or click **No** to abandon the operation.

11. After processing, the uploaded file will be shown in LoTW's **Your Activity** list with the filename selected in step 4.c above preceded by <TQSLUpl YYYYMMDD-HHMM>, where YYYY is the current year, MM is the current month, DD is the current day, HH is the current hour, and MM is the current minute.

I N D E X

FEEDBACK

Please use this form to give us your comments on this book and what you'd like to see in future editions, or e-mail us at **pubsfdbk@arrl.org** (publications feedback). If you use e-mail, please include your name, call, e-mail address and the book title, edition and printing in the body of your message. Also indicate whether or not you are an ARRL member.

Where did you purchase this book? ☐ From ARRL directly   ☐ From an ARRL dealer

Is there a dealer who carries ARRL publications within:

☐ 5 miles   ☐ 15 miles   ☐ 30 miles of your location?   ☐ Not sure.

License class:

☐ Novice   ☐ Technician   ☐ Technician with code   ☐ General   ☐ Advanced   ☐ Amateur Extra

Name _____   ARRL member? ☐ Yes ☐ No

_____ Call Sign

Address _____

City, State/Province, ZIP/Postal Code _____

Daytime Phone (   ) _____ Age _____

If licensed, how long? _____

Other hobbies _____ E-mail _____

_____

Occupation _____

For ARRL use only	YFARHFS
Edition	1 2 3 4 5 6 7 8 9 10 11 12
Printing	2 3 4 5 6 7 8 9 10 11 12

From _____

_____

_____

EDITOR, YOUR FIRST AMATEUR RADIO HF STATION
ARRL—THE NATIONAL ASSOCIATION FOR AMATEUR RADIO
225 MAIN STREET
NEWINGTON CT 06111-1494

please fold and tape